Large Print
Brain Training
PUZZLES

100 Easy to Read Puzzles

ARCTURUS

ARCTURUS

This edition published in 2018 by Arcturus Publishing Limited
26/27 Bickels Yard, 151–153 Bermondsey Street,
London SE1 3HA

Copyright © Arcturus Holdings Limited
Puzzles copyright © Puzzle Press Ltd

ISBN: 978-1-78404-577-7
AD004536NT

Printed in China

Keep your mind in trim with this wide variety of challenging puzzles. All you need to solve them is logical thinking allied to concentration.

With some puzzles taking minutes to solve and others providing tougher competition, you can exercise your mind at the same time as having fun.

So sharpen your pencils, curl up on the couch and prepare for many hours of enjoyment with this terrific selection of puzzles.

Solutions to all of the puzzles can be found at the back of the book, but try not to peek!

Domino Placement

1

A standard set of twenty-eight dominoes has been laid out as shown. Can you draw in the edges of them all? The check-box is provided as an aid, so that you can see which dominoes have been located.

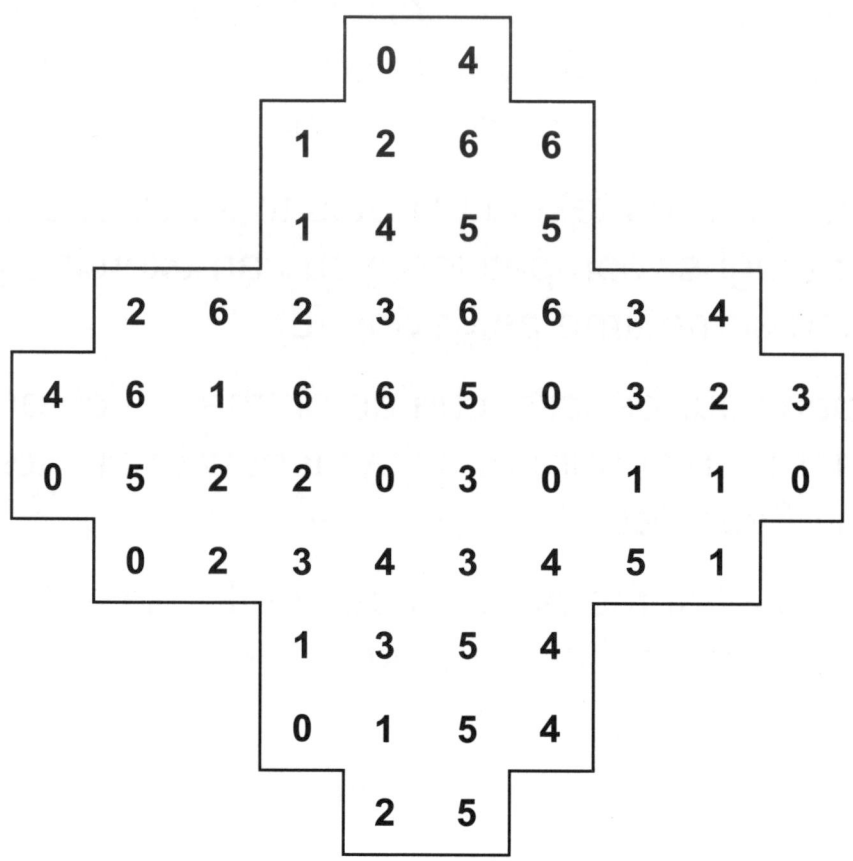

0-0	0-1	0-2	0-3	0-4	0-5	0-6	1-1	1-2	1-3	1-4	1-5	1-6	2-2

2-3	2-4	2-5	2-6	3-3	3-4	3-5	3-6	4-4	4-5	4-6	5-5	5-6	6-6

Hexagony

Can you place the hexagons into the grid, so that where any hexagon touches another along a straight line, the contents of both triangles is the same? No rotation of any hexagon is allowed!

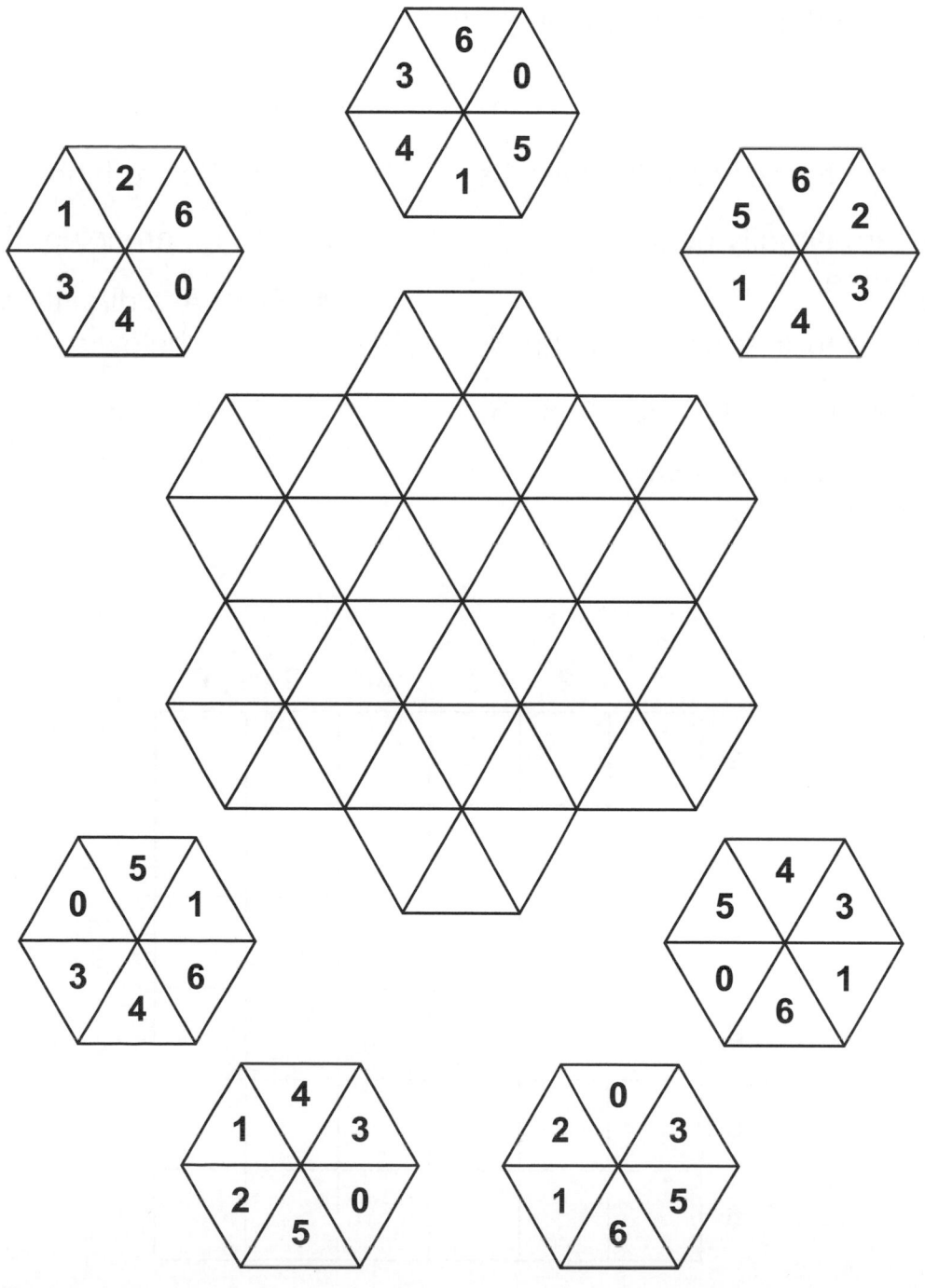

Simple as A, B, C?

Each of the small squares in the grid below contains either A, B or C. Every row, column and each of the two long diagonals has exactly two of each letter. The information in the clues refers only to the squares in that row or column. To help you solve this problem, we have provided as many clues as we think you will need! Can you tell the letter in each square?

Across

1 The Bs are further right than the Cs.

2 The Bs are directly next to each other.

3 The As are further right than the Cs.

5 Each C is next to and right of an A.

6 The Cs are directly next to each other.

Down

1 The Cs are higher than the As.

2 The Bs are lower than the As.

4 Each A is directly next to and below a C.

5 No two letters next to each other are the same.

	1	2	3	4	5	6
1						
2						
3						
4						
5						
6						

Total Concentration

The blank squares below should be filled with whole numbers between 1 and 40 inclusive, any of which may occur more than once, or not at all. The numbers in every horizontal row add up to the totals on the right, as do the two long diagonal lines; whilst those in every vertical column add up to the totals along the bottom. Can you discover the missing numbers?

								163
18	33	6	8	11	22		40	140
16	6	32	31		31		24	162
	17	38		5	12	12	4	128
34		1		28		35		153
	23		20		39	7	19	152
40		30	16	2	29	5	13	144
14	18	36		3	14	11	9	128
8	26	7	1	37			10	113
161	142	165	131	126	177	82	136	156

Shape Up

Every row and column in this grid originally contained one circle, one diamond, one square, one triangle and two blank squares, although not necessarily in that order.

Every symbol with a black arrow refers to the first of the four symbols encountered when travelling in the direction of the arrow. Every symbol with a white arrow refers to the second of the four symbols encountered in the direction of the arrow. Can you complete the original grid?

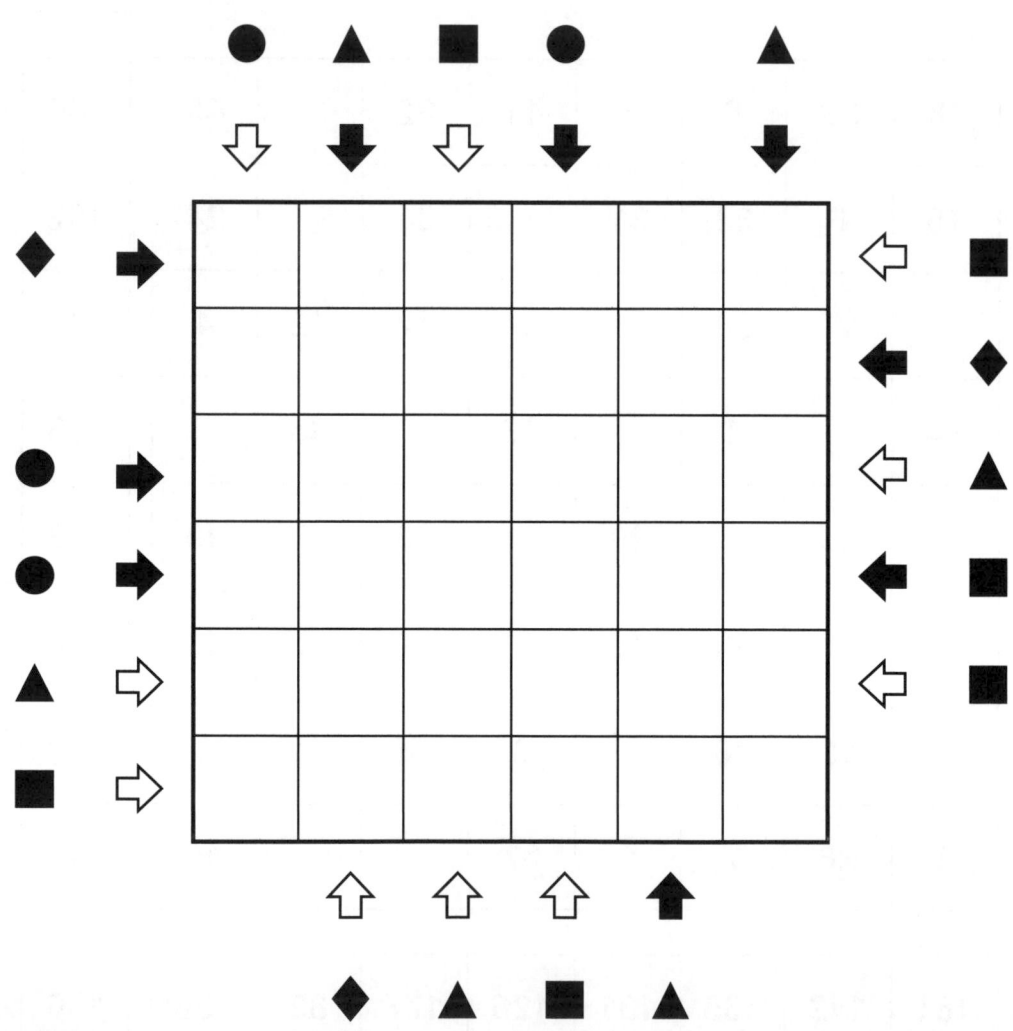

Mind Over Matter

Given that the letters are valued 1-26 according to their places in the alphabet, can you crack the mystery code to reveal the missing letter?

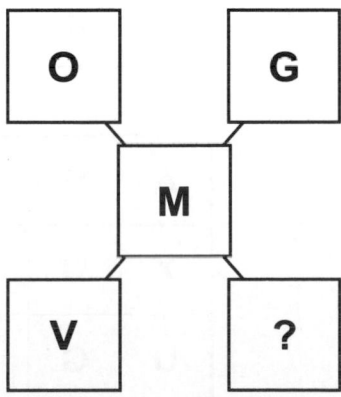

Whatever Next?

Which of the four lettered alternatives (A, B, C or D) fits most logically into the empty square?

1

D	V	E
A	G	Y
X	J	O

2

W	I	N
C	U	D
Z	F	X

3

Y	E	W
V	H	M
B	T	C

4

	?	

~~~~~~

A

B	A	D
T	E	H
Y	Z	S

B

D	F	V
H	J	C
I	P	Q

C

A	S	B
X	D	V
U	G	L

D

R	S	C
P	L	K
B	V	E

The Bottom Line

Can you fill each square in the bottom line with the correct digit? Every square in the solution contains only one digit from each of the lettered lines above, although two or more squares in the solution may contain the same digit.

At the end of every row is a score, which shows:

a   the number of digits placed in the correct finishing position on the bottom line, as indicated by a tick; and

b   the number of digits which appear on the bottom line, but in a different position, as indicated by a cross.

SCORE

A	1	2	3	4	✓ ✗
B	5	6	7	3	✓ ✗
C	8	4	1	5	✓ ✗
D	7	1	6	4	✓ ✗
E	2	8	7	6	✓ ✗
					✓✓✓✓

Combiku

Each horizontal row and vertical column should contain different shapes and different numbers.

Every square will contain one number and one shape and no combination may be repeated anywhere else in the puzzle; so, for instance, if a square contains a 3 and a star, then no other square containing a 3 will also contain a star and no other square with a star will contain a 3.

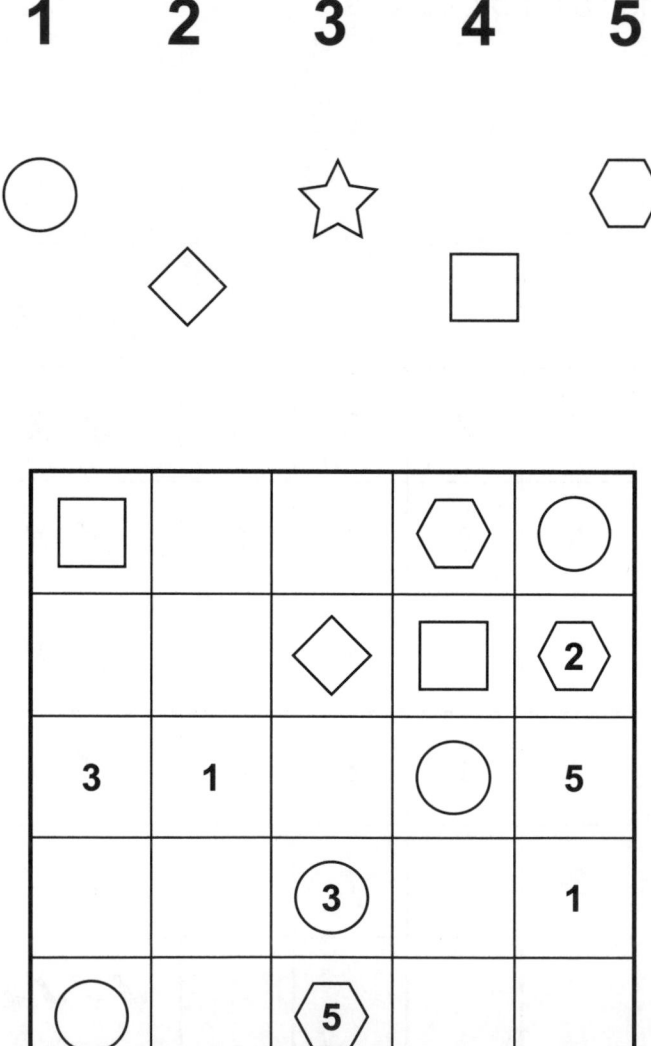

Ls in Place

Twelve L-shapes like the ones here need to be inserted in the grid and each L has one hole in it. There are three pieces of each of the four kinds shown here and any piece may be turned or flipped over before being put in the grid. No pieces of the same kind touch, even at a corner.

The pieces fit together so well that you cannot see any spaces between them; only the holes show. Can you tell where the Ls are?

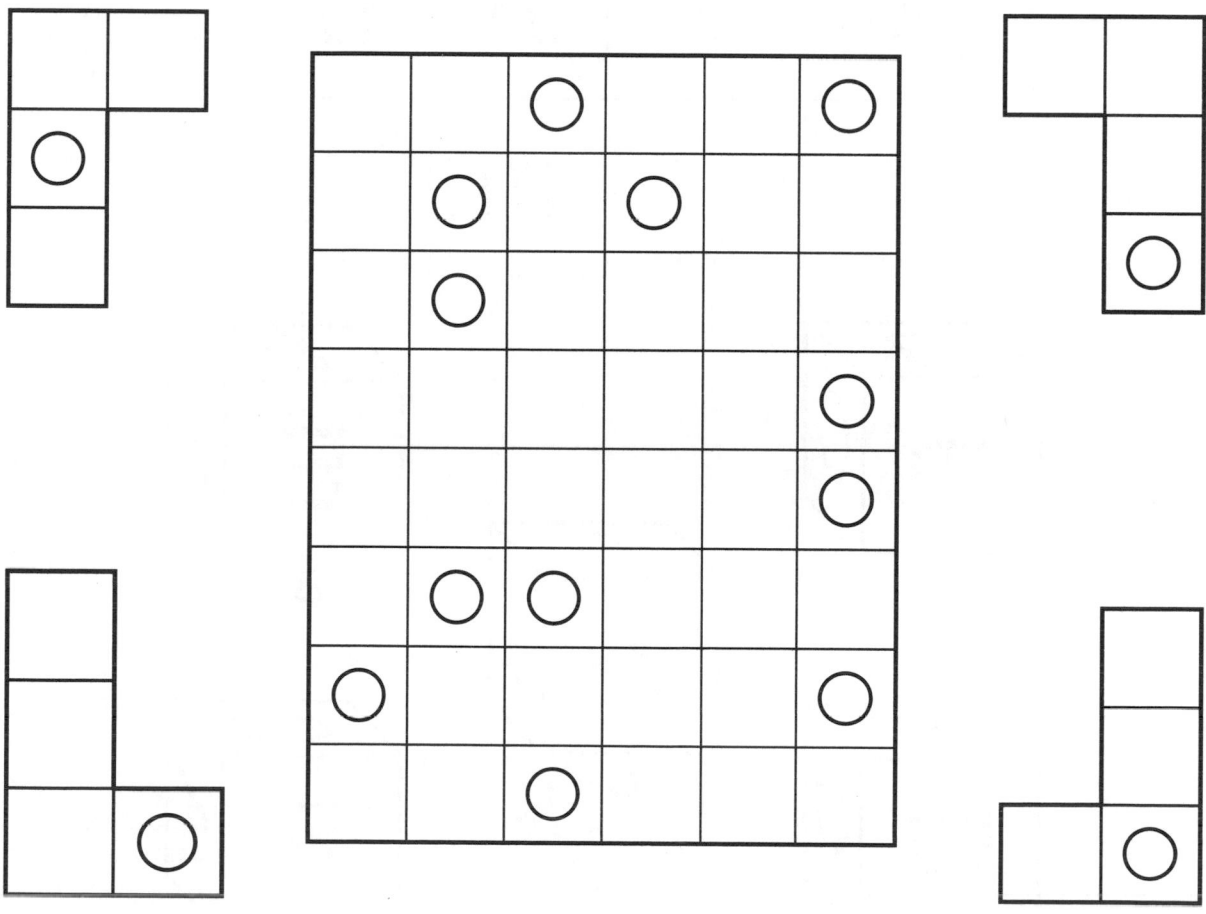

Box Clever

When the box below is folded to form a cube, just one of the five options (A, B, C, D or E) can be produced. Which?

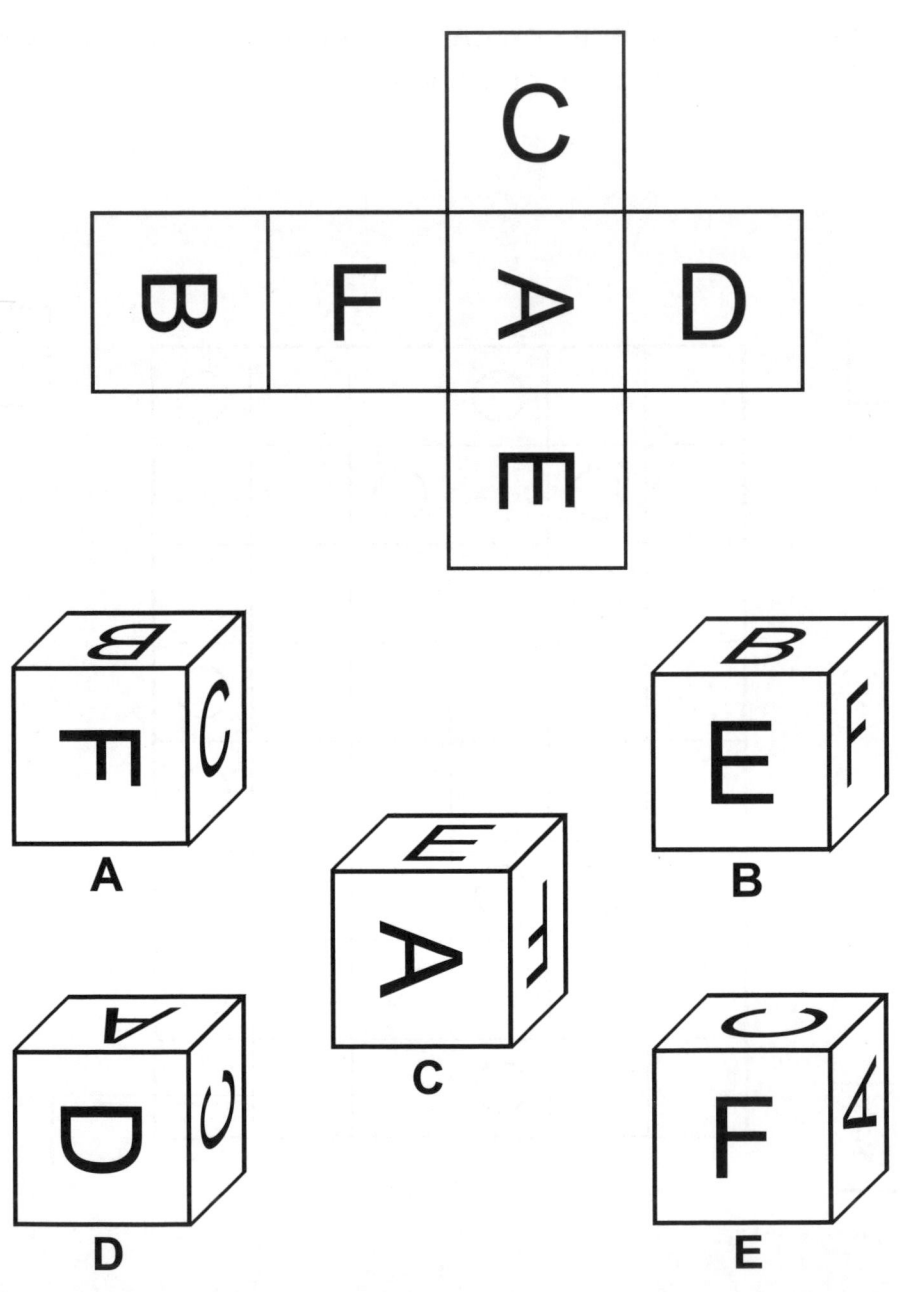

Latin Square

The grid should be filled with numbers from 1 to 6, so that each number appears just once in every row and column. The clues refer to the digit totals in the squares, for example A 1 2 3 = 6 means that the numbers in squares A1, A2 and A3 add up to 6.

1 E 3 4 5 = 12

2 F 4 5 = 7

3 B C D 1 = 6

4 B C 2 = 8

5 A B 3 = 4

6 A B 4 = 9

7 C D 5 = 7

8 C D 6 = 11

9 A 1 2 = 7

10 B 5 6 = 7

11 C 3 4 = 8

	A	B	C	D	E	F
1						
2						
3						
4						
5						
6						

Symbolism

Each of these squares should contain one or more symbols from the numbered square to the left of its particular horizontal row, plus one or more symbols from the lettered square above its particular vertical column. However, one square doesn't follow this rule. Which is the odd one out?

	A ◀ ≈	B ♣ $	C ‡ ¿	D ♦ #	E ♪ ¶	F Σ ☼
1 ∩ π	π ◀ ≈	∩ π ♣	¿ ‡ ∩	♦# ∩	¶ ∩ π	Σ ∩
2 ♠ ß	≈ ♠ ß	♠ ♣ ß	¿ ß	♠ #♦	ß ♪ ¶	♠ ☼ ß
3 £ ▶	£ ◀ ▶	£ $ ▶	▶ ¿ £	# ▶	♪ £ ▶	▶ ☼
4 Ω §	§ ≈ Ω	$ Ω §	Ω‡ §	§ # Ω	§ ♪	Ω ☼
5 △ ♥	◀ △	♥ $	¿ △	♦ ♥	¶ ♥ ♪	△ Σ
6 ▲ ♫	≈ ♫ ▲	▲ ♣ $	‡ ▲	♫ ▲	♪ ♫	Σ ♫ ▲
7 ▼ φ	φ ◀	♣ ▼ φ	φ ‡	▼ # φ	¶ φ	Σ φ

Can you place the vessels into the diagram? Some parts of vessels or sea squares have already been filled in. A number to the right or below a row or column refers to the number of occupied squares in that row or column.

Any vessel may be positioned horizontally or vertically, but no part of a vessel touches part of any other vessel, either horizontally, vertically or diagonally.

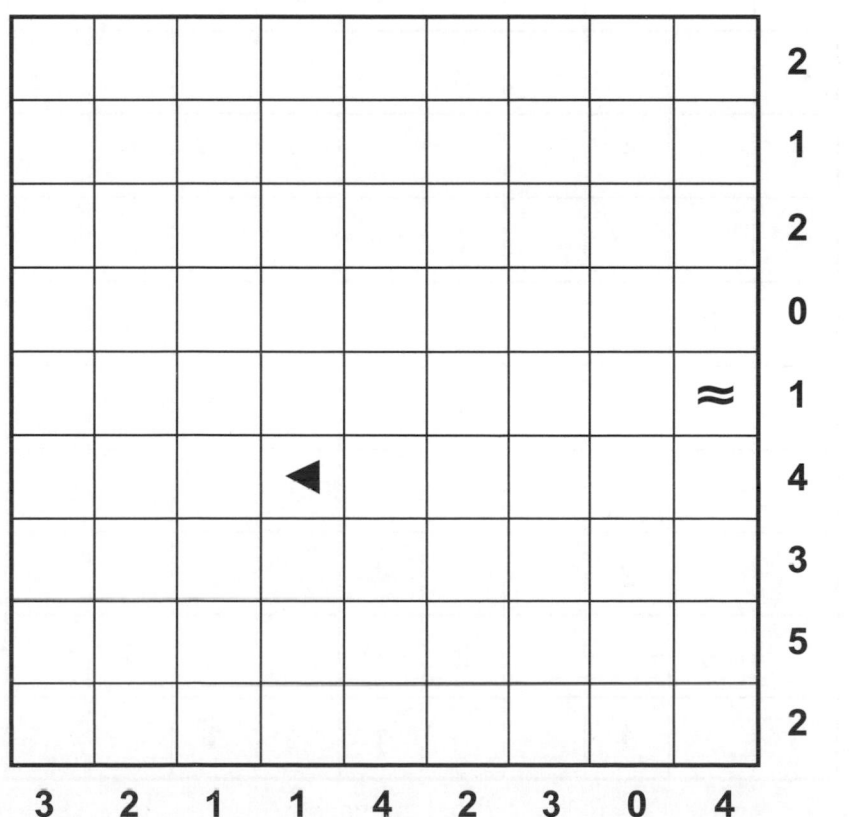

Coin Collecting

In this puzzle, an amateur coin collector has been out with his metal detector, searching for booty. He didn't have time to dig up all the coins he found, so has made a grid map, showing their locations, in the hope that if he loses the map, at least no-one else will understand it... However, he didn't count on YOU coming across the strange grid (as seen here). Will you be able to discover the correct number of coins and their precise locations?

Those squares containing numbers are empty, but where a number appears in a square, it indicates how many coins are located in the squares (up to a maximum of eight) surrounding the numbered one, touching it at any corner or side. There is only one coin in any individual square.

Place a circle into every square containing a coin.

	0				1	2			
				2				1	
1		1				2		3	
				1		1			
	0		1				2	4	
2				4		3			
					5				
		2			4			3	
	3			2				0	
1		1			1		1		

Slitherlink

Draw a single continuous loop, by connecting the dots. No line may cross the path of another.

The figure inside each set of any four surrounding dots indicates the total number of surrounding lines.

Balancing the Scales

Given that scales A and B balance perfectly, how many hearts are needed to balance scale C?

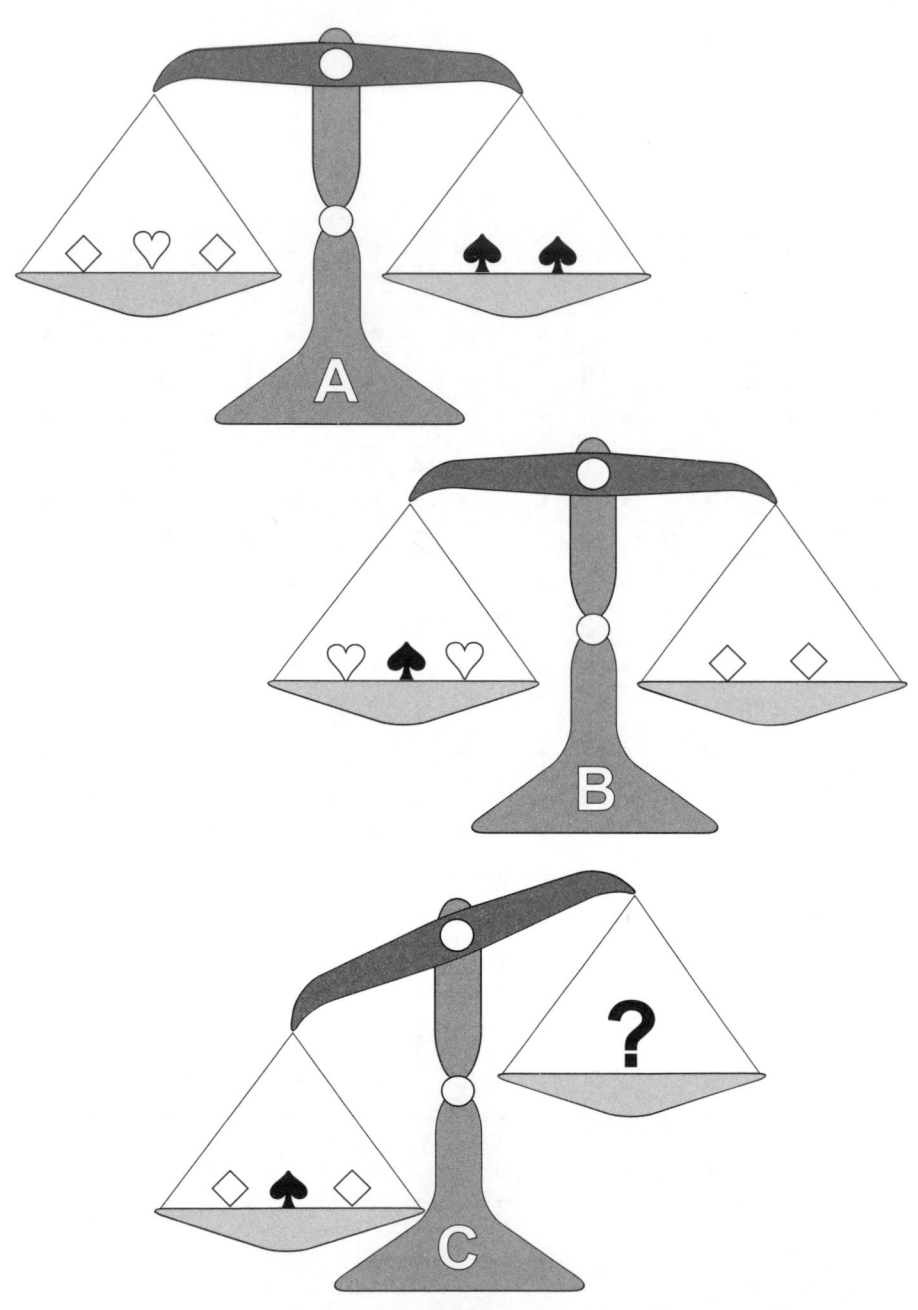

Every row and column of this grid should contain one each of the letters A, B, C, D, E and F. In addition, each of the six shapes (marked by thicker lines) should also contain one each of the letters A, B, C, D, E and F. Can you complete the grid?

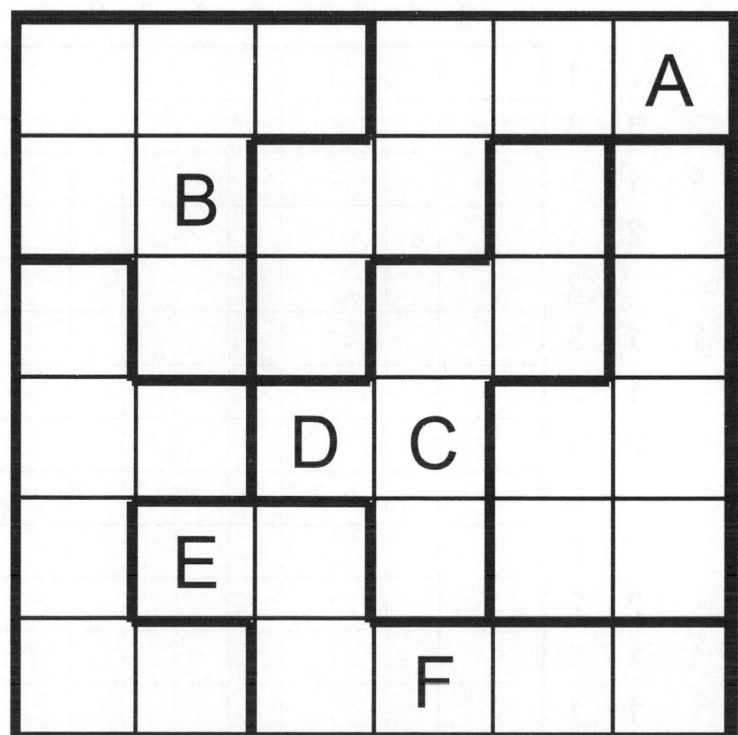

Piecework

Place all twelve of the pieces into the grid. Any may be rotated or flipped over, but none may touch another, not even diagonally. The numbers outside the grid refer to the number of consecutive black squares; and each block is separated from the others by at least one white square. For instance, '3 2' could refer to a row with none, one or more white squares, then three black squares, then at least one white square, then two more black squares, followed by any number of white squares.

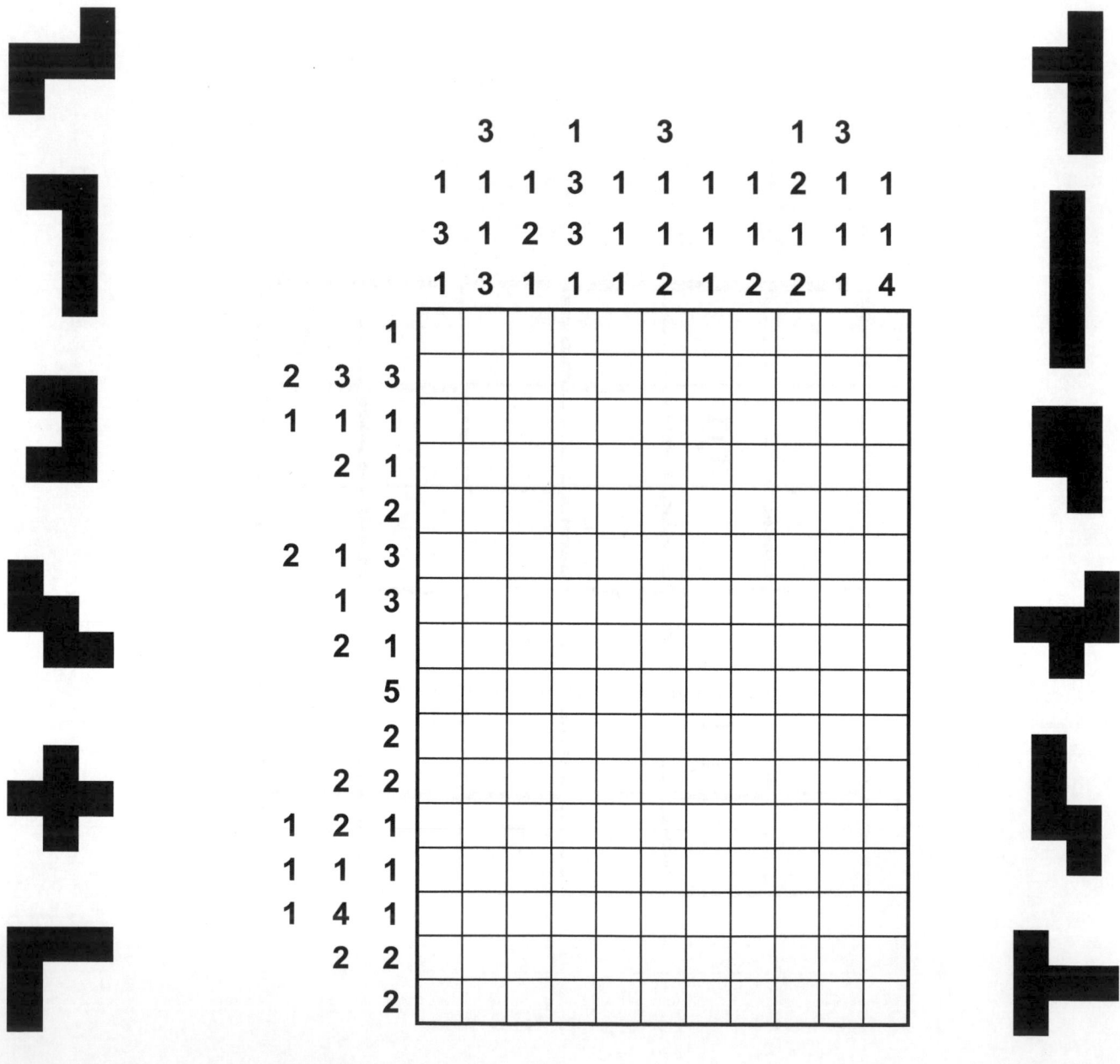

Tile Twister

Place the eight tiles into the puzzle grid so that all adjacent numbers on each tile match up. Tiles may be rotated through 360 degrees, but none may be flipped over.

1	3
2	1

2	2
4	3

2	4
3	1

2	4
1	3

				4	2
				2	3

1	4
4	2

1	2
2	2

1	4
2	4

1	3
4	4

Domino Placement

A standard set of twenty-eight dominoes has been laid out as shown. Can you draw in the edges of them all? The check-box is provided as an aid, so that you can see which dominoes have been located.

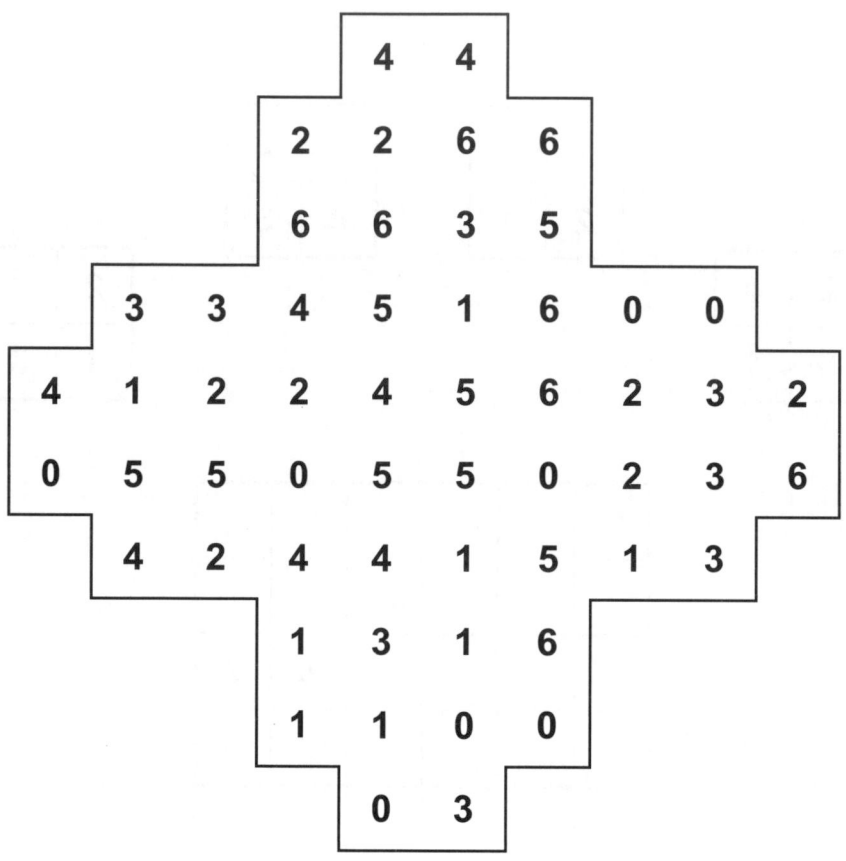

0-0	0-1	0-2	0-3	0-4	0-5	0-6	1-1	1-2	1-3	1-4	1-5	1-6	2-2

2-3	2-4	2-5	2-6	3-3	3-4	3-5	3-6	4-4	4-5	4-6	5-5	5-6	6-6

Hexagony

Can you place the hexagons into the grid, so that where any hexagon touches another along a straight line, the contents of both triangles is the same? No rotation of any hexagon is allowed!

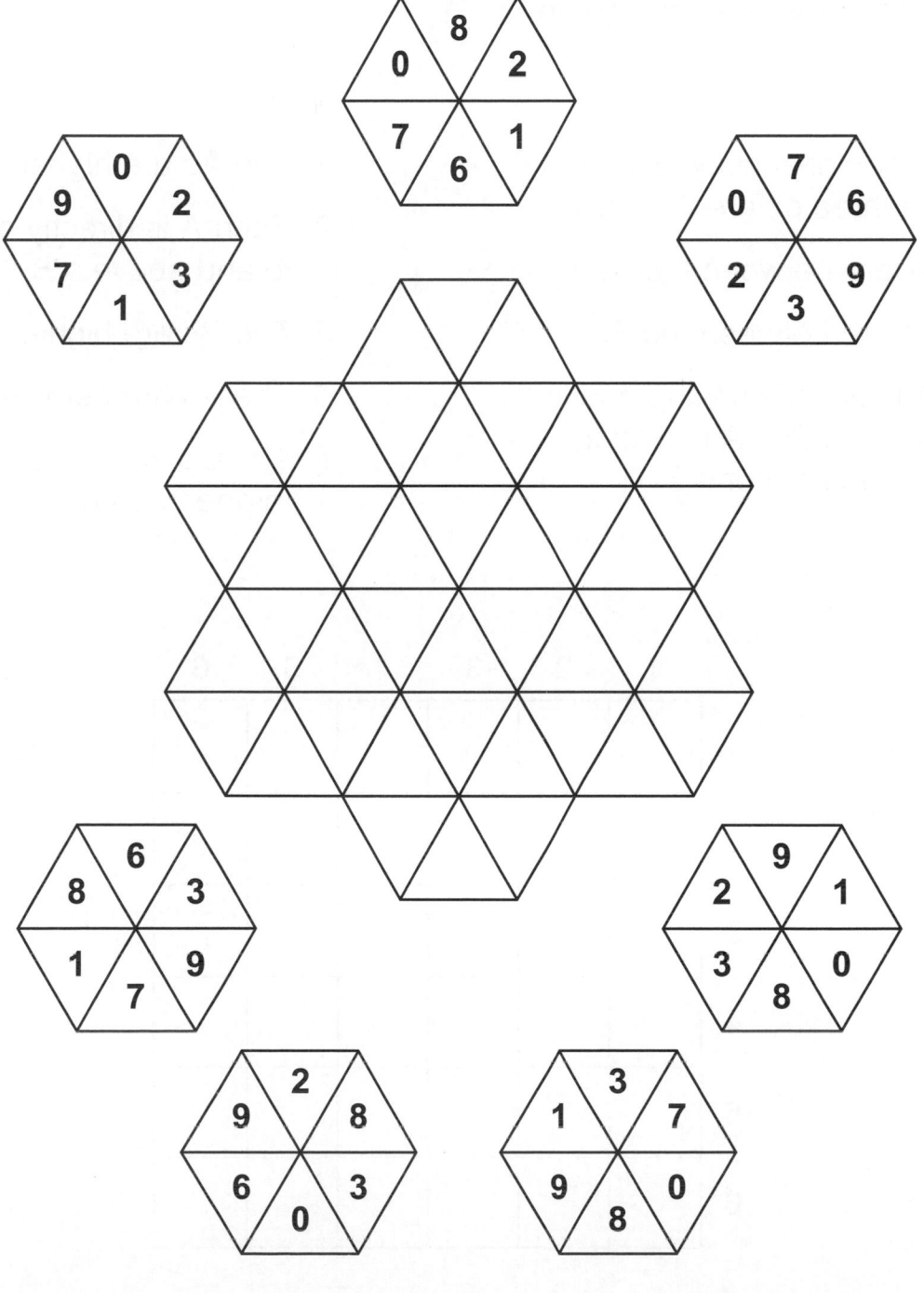

Simple as A, B, C?

Each of the small squares in the grid below contains either A, B or C. Every row, column and each of the two long diagonals has exactly two of each letter. The information in the clues refers only to the squares in that row or column. To help you solve this problem, we have provided as many clues as we think you will need! Can you tell the letter in each square?

Across

1 Any three consecutive squares contain three different letters.

2 The Bs are between the As.

3 The Cs are between the Bs.

5 One A is directly next to and left of a B. The other A is directly next to and right of a B.

Down

1 The As are higher than the Cs.

2 Each A is directly next to and above a B.

3 The Bs are higher than the Cs.

5 The As are between the Bs.

6 The Cs are adjacent to one another.

Total Concentration

The blank squares below should be filled with whole numbers between 1 and 40 inclusive, any of which may occur more than once, or not at all. The numbers in every horizontal row add up to the totals on the right, as do the two long diagonal lines; whilst those in every vertical column add up to the totals along the bottom. Can you discover the missing numbers?

								109
14	25	11		37	32	34	2	164
		13	5	34	25	2	26	126
35	26		6	5	1	22		159
1	18	21	34	40				163
26	21			19		19	11	180
37		30	34		34	2	24	188
15	1	37	38		20	6	4	151
	12		33		21	10	4	116
144	130	182	186	198	174	122	111	161

Shape Up

Every row and column in this grid originally contained one circle, one diamond, one square, one triangle and two blank squares, although not necessarily in that order.

Every symbol with a black arrow refers to the first of the four symbols encountered when travelling in the direction of the arrow. Every symbol with a white arrow refers to the second of the four symbols encountered in the direction of the arrow. Can you complete the original grid?

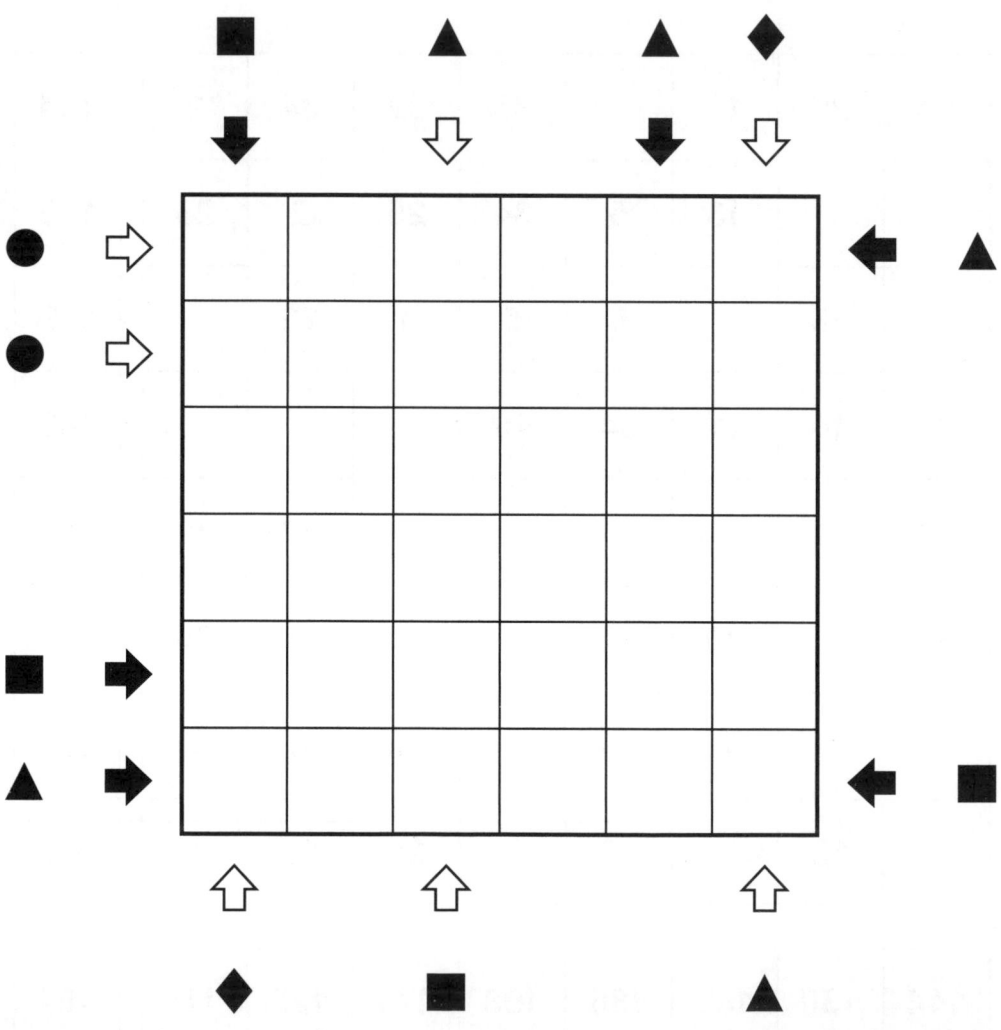

Given that the letters are valued 1-26 according to their places in the alphabet, can you crack the mystery code to reveal the missing letter?

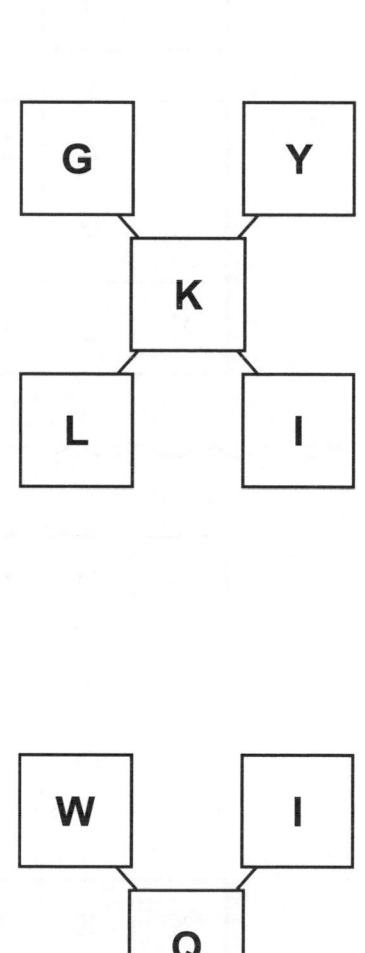

Whatever Next?

Which of the four lettered alternatives (A, B, C or D) fits most logically into the empty square?

1

J	J	J
J	J	J
J	J	J

2

Y	Y	Y
Y	Y	Y
Y	Y	Y

3

E	E	E
E	E	E
E	E	E

4

?

A

O	O	O
O	O	O
O	O	O

B

D	D	D
D	D	D
D	D	D

C

X	X	X
X	X	X
X	X	X

D

N	N	N
N	N	N
N	N	N

The Bottom Line

Can you fill each square in the bottom line with the correct digit? Every square in the solution contains only one digit from each of the lettered lines above, although two or more squares in the solution may contain the same digit.

At the end of every row is a score, which shows:

    a   the number of digits placed in the correct finishing position on the bottom line, as indicated by a tick; and

    b   the number of digits which appear on the bottom line, but in a different position, as indicated by a cross.

SCORE

A	1	2	3	4	✗ ✗
B	4	5	6	1	✗ ✗
C	7	1	2	6	✓
D	2	8	4	5	✓ ✗
E	7	2	8	3	✓ ✗
					✓✓✓✓

Combiku

Each horizontal row and vertical column should contain different shapes and different numbers.

Every square will contain one number and one shape and no combination may be repeated anywhere else in the puzzle; so, for instance, if a square contains a 3 and a star, then no other square containing a 3 will also contain a star and no other square with a star will contain a 3.

1   2   3   4   5

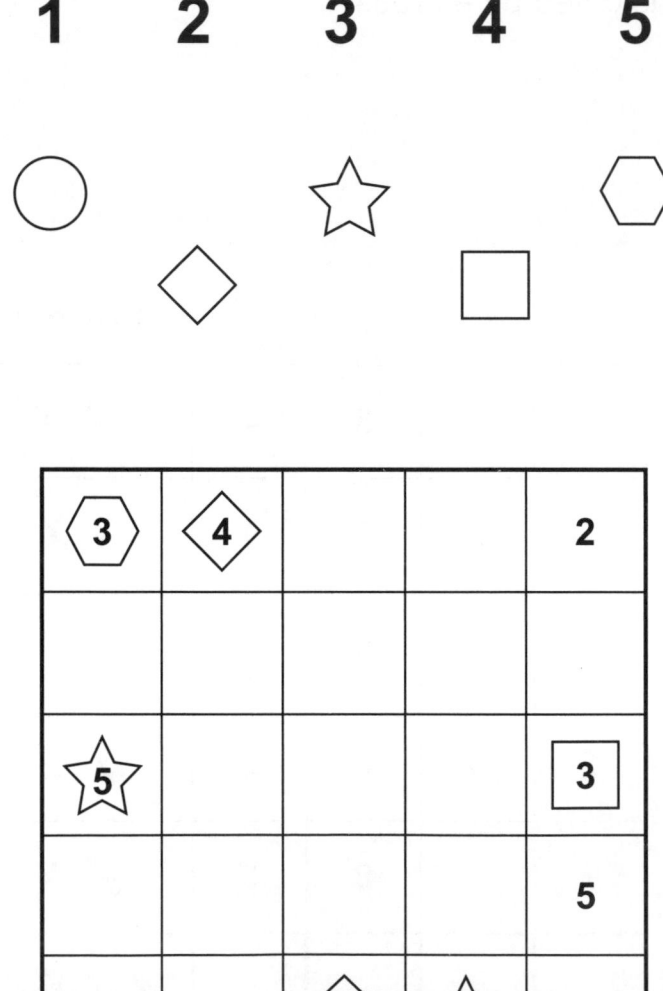

Ls in Place

Twelve L-shapes like the ones here need to be inserted in the grid and each L has one hole in it. There are three pieces of each of the four kinds shown here and any piece may be turned or flipped over before being put in the grid. No pieces of the same kind touch, even at a corner.

The pieces fit together so well that you cannot see any spaces between them; only the holes show. Can you tell where the Ls are?

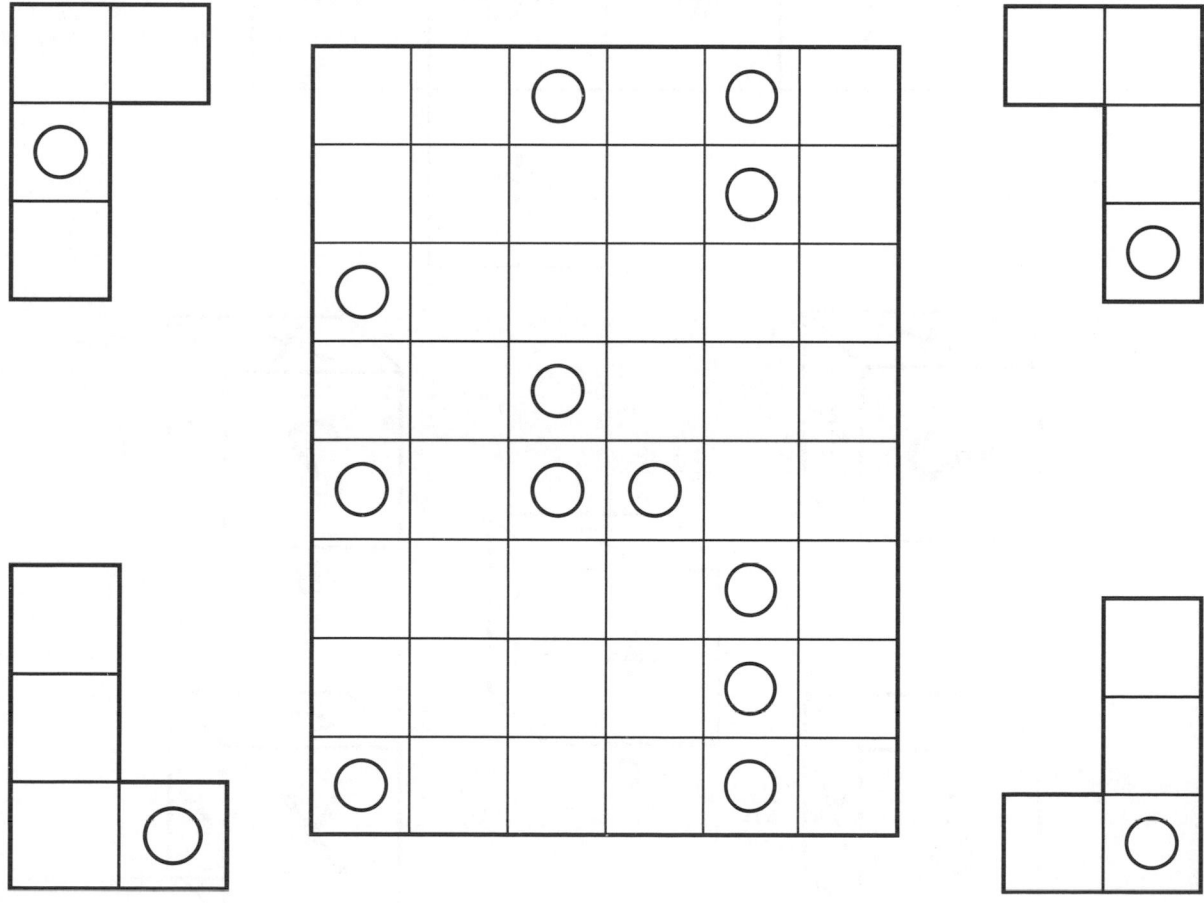

Box Clever

When the box below is folded to form a cube, just one of the five options (A, B, C, D or E) can be produced. Which?

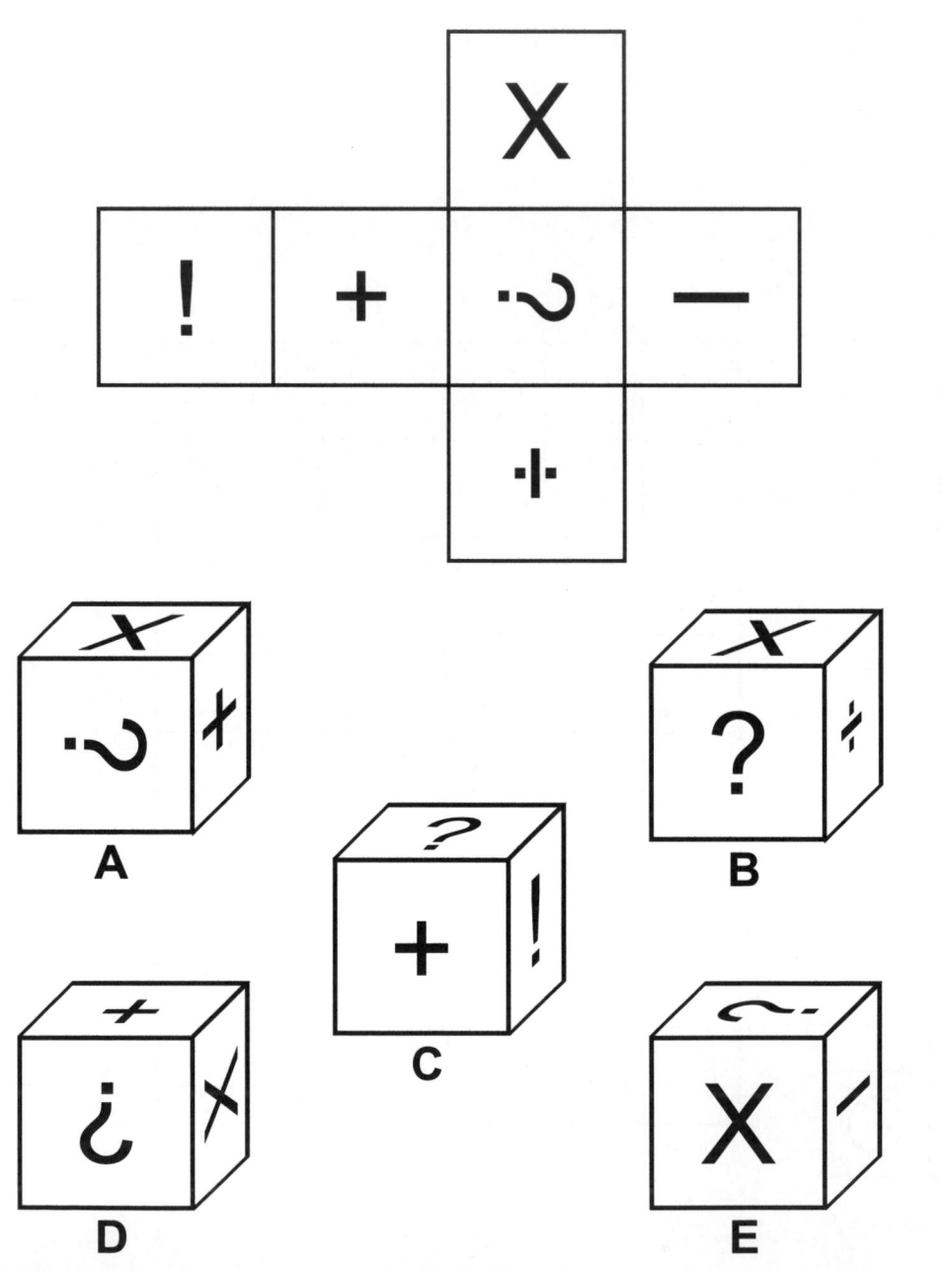

Latin Square

The grid should be filled with numbers from 1 to 6, so that each number appears just once in every row and column. The clues refer to the digit totals in the squares, for example A 1 2 3 = 6 means that the numbers in squares A1, A2 and A3 add up to 6.

1 B 1 2 3 = 8

2 C 4 5 6 = 13

3 D 1 2 = 6

4 E 5 6 = 3

5 F 3 4 = 4

6 E F 1 = 6

7 E F 2 = 10

8 C D 3 = 10

9 D E 4 = 5

10 A B 5 = 4

11 A B 6 = 9

	A	B	C	D	E	F
1						
2						
3						
4						
5						
6						

Symbolism

Each of these squares should contain one or more symbols from the numbered square to the left of its particular horizontal row, plus one or more symbols from the lettered square above its particular vertical column. However, one square doesn't follow this rule. Which is the odd one out?

		A ◄ ≈	B ♣ $	C ‡ ¿	D ♦ #	E ♪ ¶	F Σ ☼
1	∩ π	≈ π	$ π ∩	‡ ∩ π	# ♦ ∩	♪ π ¶	π Σ ☼
2	♠ ß	≈ ♠ ß	♠ ♣ $	¿ ß ‡	ß ♦ #	♪ ♠	♠ Σ
3	£ ►	◄ £ ►	£ ♣	► ¿ ‡	# £	♪ ►	Σ ►
4	Ω §	◄ Ω ≈	Ω § ♣	¿ §	♦ § Ω	¶ Ω	§ Σ
5	△ ♥	◄ ≈ △	♣ ♥ $	△ ‡	♥ #	♥ △	♥ Σ
6	▲ ♫	◄ ▲	▲ $	▲ ¿	# ♫	¶ ▲	♫ Σ
7	▼ φ	▼ ◄	▼ ♣	¿ φ	φ ▼ ♦	φ ♪	▼ ☼

Battleships

Can you place the vessels into the diagram? Some parts of vessels or sea squares have already been filled in. A number to the right or below a row or column refers to the number of occupied squares in that row or column.

Any vessel may be positioned horizontally or vertically, but no part of a vessel touches part of any other vessel, either horizontally, vertically or diagonally.

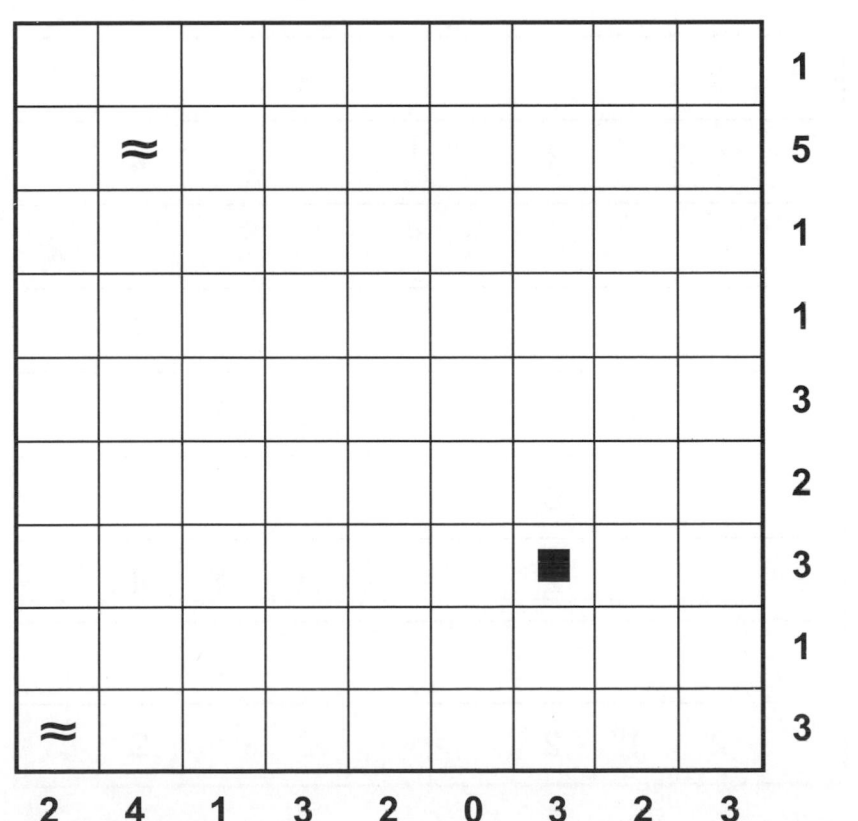

Coin Collecting

In this puzzle, an amateur coin collector has been out with his metal detector, searching for booty. He didn't have time to dig up all the coins he found, so has made a grid map, showing their locations, in the hope that if he loses the map, at least no-one else will understand it... However, he didn't count on YOU coming across the strange grid (as seen here). Will you be able to discover the correct number of coins and their precise locations?

Those squares containing numbers are empty, but where a number appears in a square, it indicates how many coins are located in the squares (up to a maximum of eight) surrounding the numbered one, touching it at any corner or side. There is only one coin in any individual square.

Place a circle into every square containing a coin.

						2		2	
	0	1			3	4		3	
	0		1					4	
				1					2
2							3	2	
		4				2	3		
2			0						
2			2	1		3	4	4	
							3		
	2	1	2			3		2	

Slitherlink

Draw a single continuous loop, by connecting the dots. No line may cross the path of another.

The figure inside each set of any four surrounding dots indicates the total number of surrounding lines.

Balancing the Scales

Given that scales A and B balance perfectly, how many diamonds are needed to balance scale C?

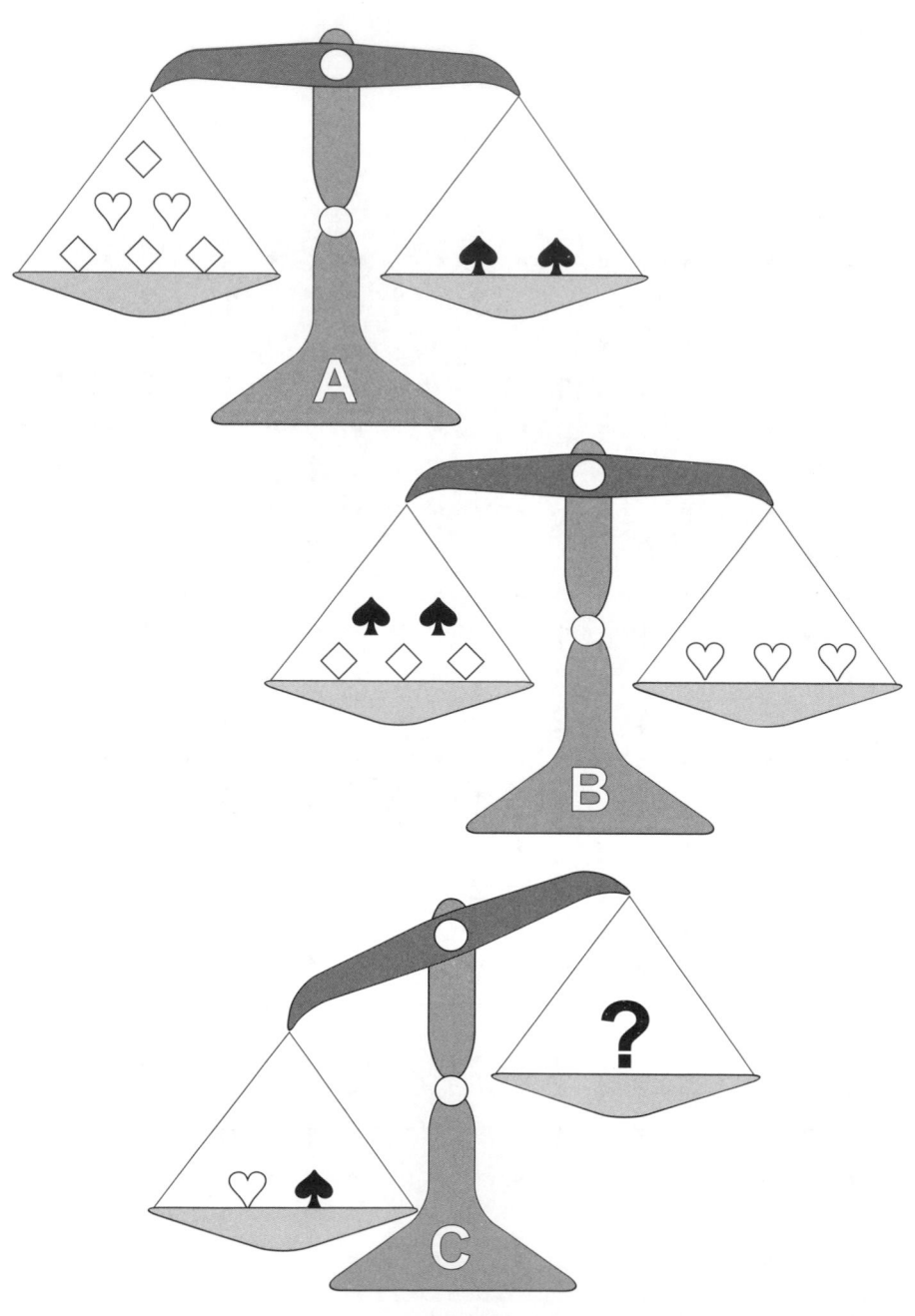

Every row and column of this grid should contain one each of the letters A, B, C, D, E and F. In addition, each of the six shapes (marked by thicker lines) should also contain one each of the letters A, B, C, D, E and F. Can you complete the grid?

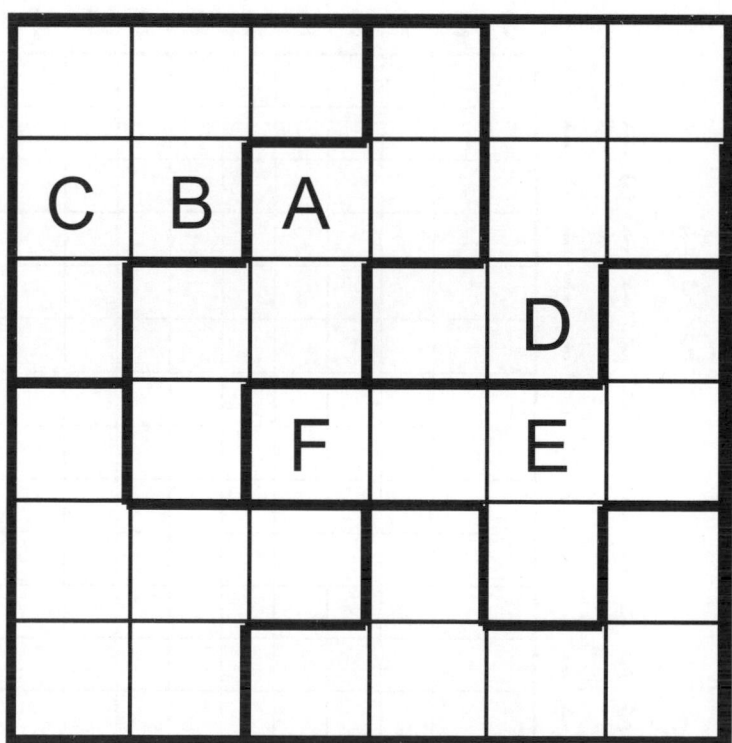

Piecework

Place all twelve of the pieces into the grid. Any may be rotated or flipped over, but none may touch another, not even diagonally. The numbers outside the grid refer to the number of consecutive black squares; and each block is separated from the others by at least one white square. For instance, '3 2' could refer to a row with none, one or more white squares, then three black squares, then at least one white square, then two more black squares, followed by any number of white squares.

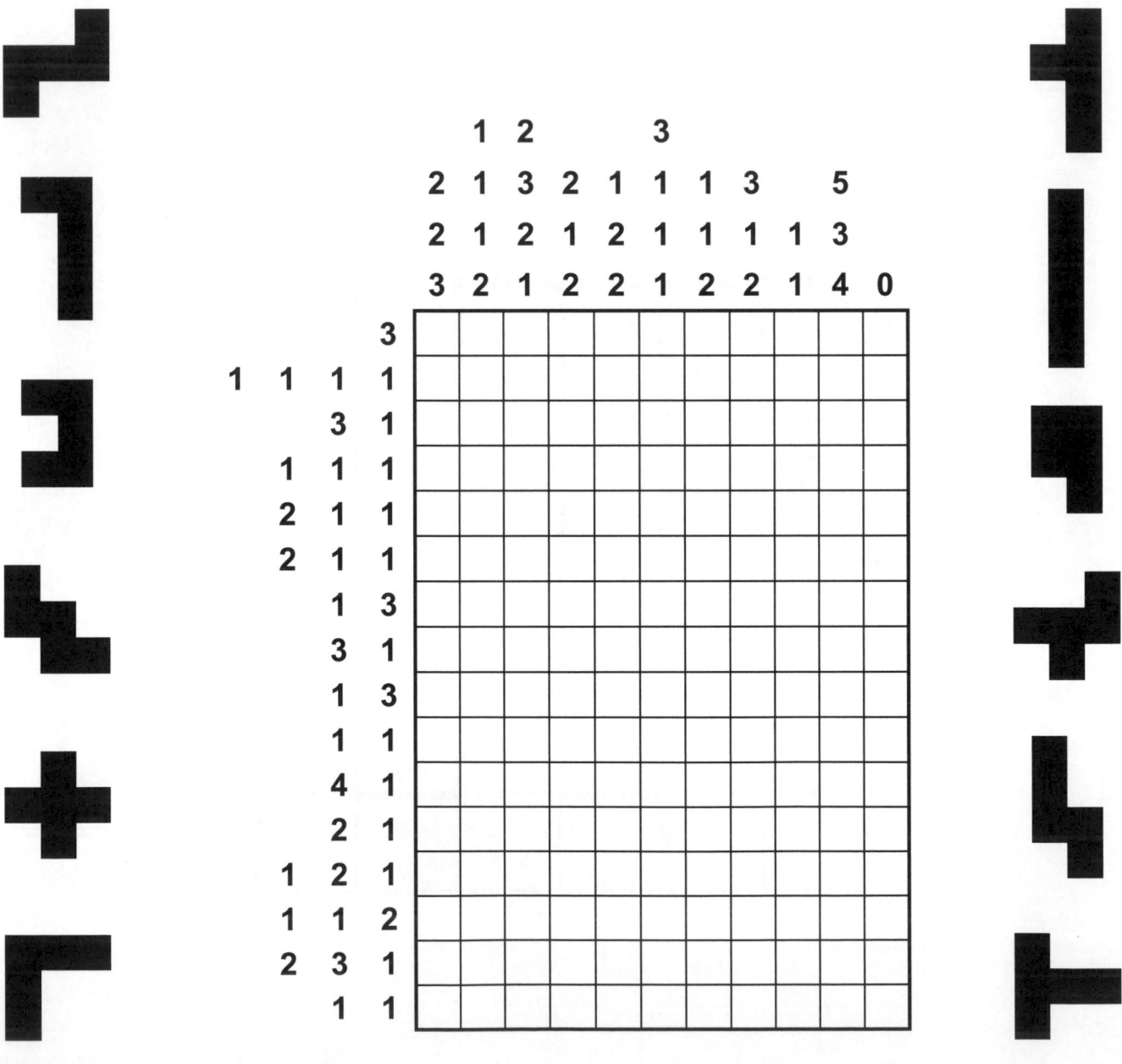

Tile Twister

Place the eight tiles into the puzzle grid so that all adjacent numbers on each tile match up. Tiles may be rotated through 360 degrees, but none may be flipped over.

2	3
2	1

4	4
2	3

2	1
4	3

2	2
4	2

The central grid contains:

		4	2		
		3	2		

3	1
3	4

3	3
1	4

4	1
2	1

2	2
3	3

Domino Placement

A standard set of twenty-eight dominoes has been laid out as shown. Can you draw in the edges of them all? The check-box is provided as an aid, so that you can see which dominoes have been located.

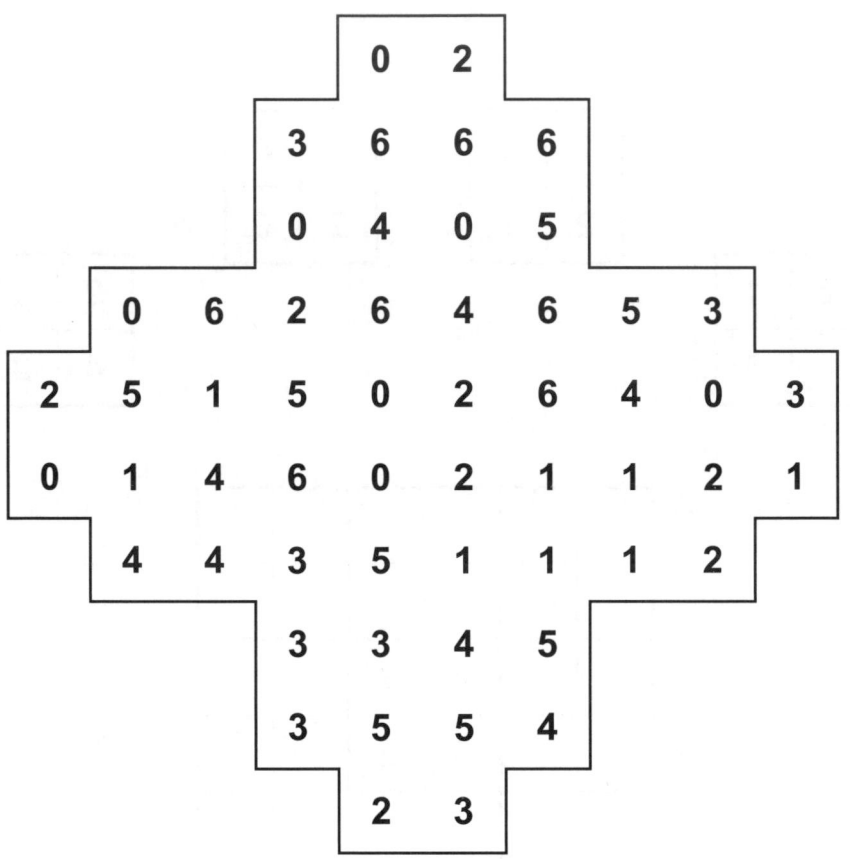

0-0	0-1	0-2	0-3	0-4	0-5	0-6	1-1	1-2	1-3	1-4	1-5	1-6	2-2

2-3	2-4	2-5	2-6	3-3	3-4	3-5	3-6	4-4	4-5	4-6	5-5	5-6	6-6

Hexagony

Can you place the hexagons into the grid, so that where any hexagon touches another along a straight line, the contents of both triangles is the same? No rotation of any hexagon is allowed!

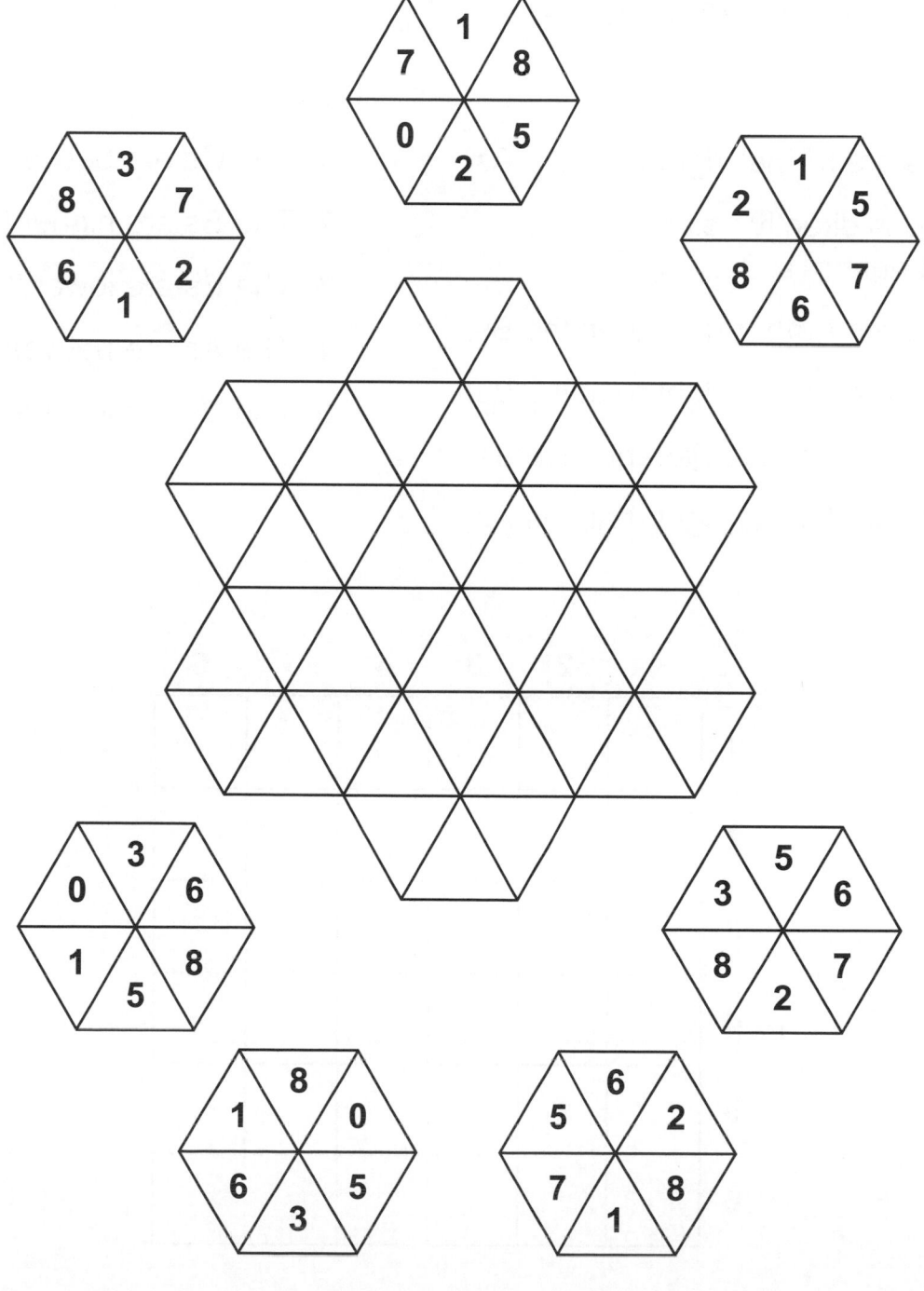

Simple as A, B, C?

Each of the small squares in the grid below contains either A, B or C. Every row, column and each of the two long diagonals has exactly two of each letter. The information in the clues refers only to the squares in that row or column. To help you solve this problem, we have provided as many clues as we think you will need! Can you tell the letter in each square?

Across

1 The Bs are further right than the As.

2 Each B is directly next to and right of a C.

3 The As are further right than the Bs.

4 The As are further right than the Bs.

5 The Cs are not in adjacent squares.

6 The Bs are further right than the As.

Down

1 The Cs are between the As.

2 The Bs are higher than the Cs.

3 The Bs are lower than the Cs.

4 The As are between the Bs.

6 The Bs are lower than the Cs.

	1	2	3	4	5	6
1						
2						
3						
4						
5						
6						

Total Concentration

The blank squares below should be filled with whole numbers between 1 and 40 inclusive, any of which may occur more than once, or not at all. The numbers in every horizontal row add up to the totals on the right, as do the two long diagonal lines; whilst those in every vertical column add up to the totals along the bottom. Can you discover the missing numbers?

								127
5	32	26			6	24	14	152
13	30	25		29			13	182
	9	31	2	31	31	11		147
29	9		2	17		22	22	145
24			9		30	24	2	147
		15	1	25	39	35	30	175
21	3	33	38	17	16	37		173
14	25	29		32	13		26	188
124	150	177	141	193	180	204	140	203

Shape Up

Every row and column in this grid originally contained one circle, one diamond, one square, one triangle and two blank squares, although not necessarily in that order.

Every symbol with a black arrow refers to the first of the four symbols encountered when travelling in the direction of the arrow. Every symbol with a white arrow refers to the second of the four symbols encountered in the direction of the arrow. Can you complete the original grid?

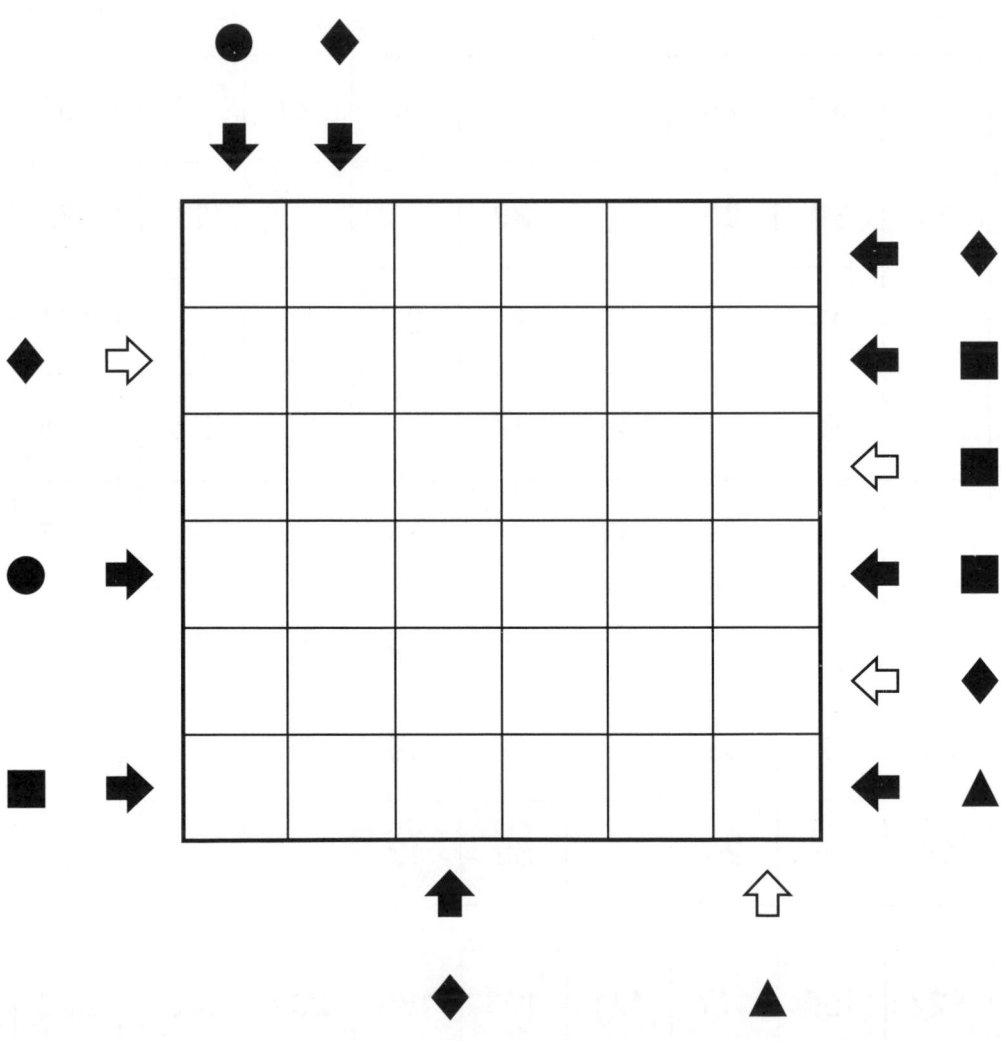

Mind Over Matter

Given that the letters are valued 1-26 according to their places in the alphabet, can you crack the mystery code to reveal the missing letter?

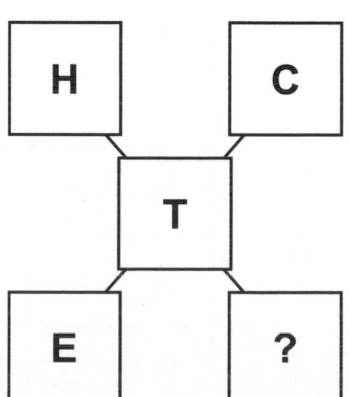

Whatever Next?

Which of the four lettered alternatives (A, B, C or D) fits most logically into the empty square?

1

E	N	P
A	G	R
L	H	E

2

D	M	O
C	I	T
N	J	G

3

C	L	N
E	K	V
P	L	I

4

	?	

A

B	K	M
G	M	X
S	N	K

B

B	J	M
G	N	X
R	N	K

C

B	J	M
H	M	X
S	O	K

D

B	K	M
G	M	X
R	N	K

The Bottom Line

Can you fill each square in the bottom line with the correct digit? Every square in the solution contains only one digit from each of the lettered lines above, although two or more squares in the solution may contain the same digit.

At the end of every row is a score, which shows:

a   the number of digits placed in the correct finishing position on the bottom line, as indicated by a tick; and

b   the number of digits which appear on the bottom line, but in a different position, as indicated by a cross.

SCORE

A	1	2	3	4	✗ ✗
B	5	2	6	1	✓ ✗
C	6	1	7	4	✓ ✗
D	1	6	3	8	✓ ✗
E	6	5	7	8	✓ ✗
					✓✓✓✓

Combiku

Each horizontal row and vertical column should contain different shapes and different numbers.

Every square will contain one number and one shape and no combination may be repeated anywhere else in the puzzle; so, for instance, if a square contains a 3 and a star, then no other square containing a 3 will also contain a star and no other square with a star will contain a 3.

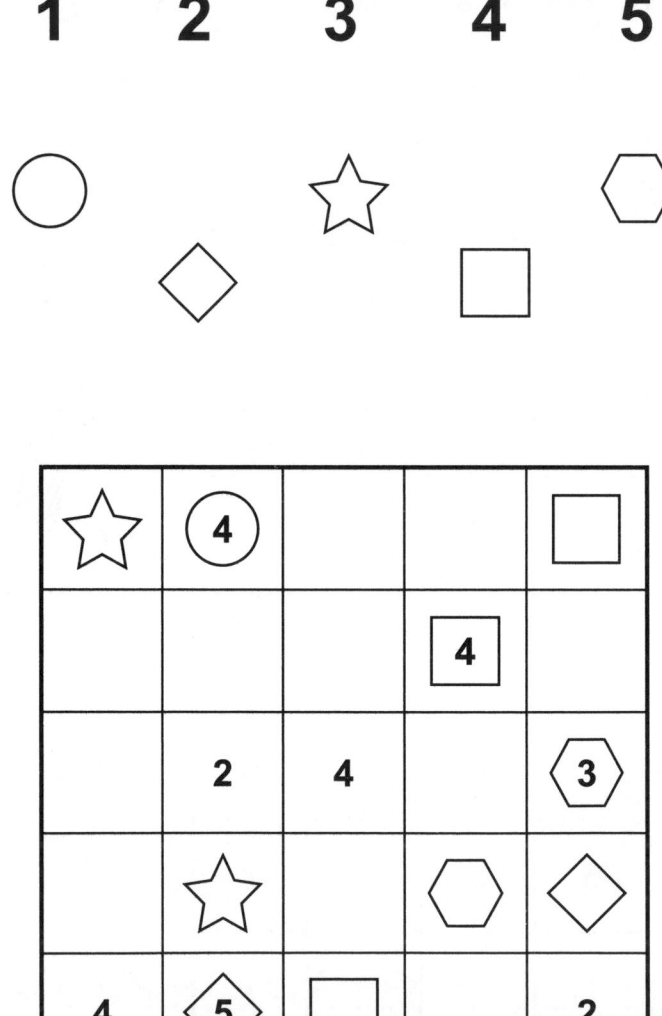

Ls in Place

Twelve L-shapes like the ones here need to be inserted in the grid and each L has one hole in it. There are three pieces of each of the four kinds shown here and any piece may be turned or flipped over before being put in the grid. No pieces of the same kind touch, even at a corner.

The pieces fit together so well that you cannot see any spaces between them; only the holes show. Can you tell where the Ls are?

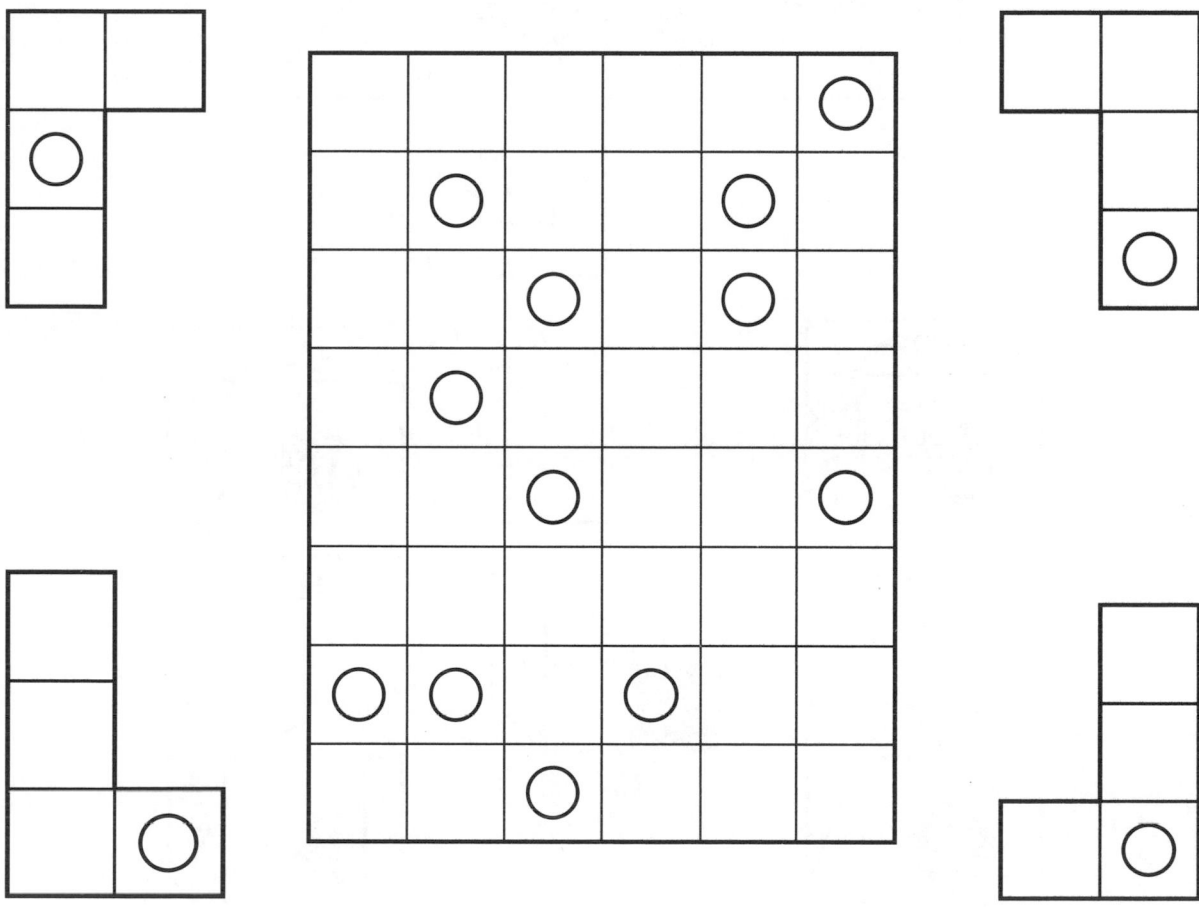

Box Clever

When the box below is folded to form a cube, just one of the five options (A, B, C, D or E) can be produced. Which?

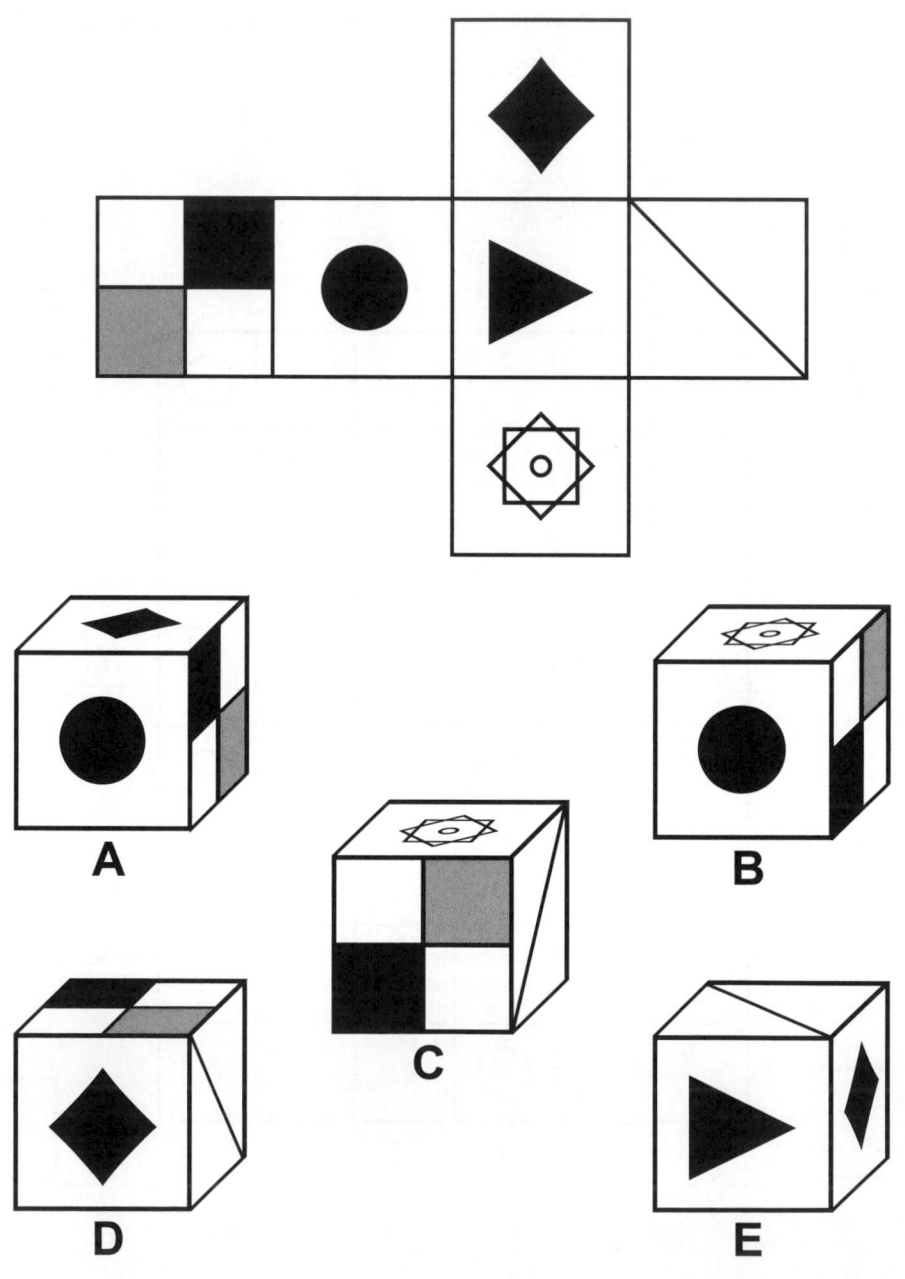

A

B

C

D

E

Latin Square

The grid should be filled with numbers from 1 to 6, so that each number appears just once in every row and column. The clues refer to the digit totals in the squares, for example A 1 2 3 = 6 means that the numbers in squares A1, A2 and A3 add up to 6.

1 E 1 2 = 9

2 F 2 3 4 = 6

3 A B 1 = 8

4 A B C 2 = 10

5 A B 3 = 10

6 A B 4 = 8

7 C D 5 = 11

8 E F 6 = 10

9 A 5 6 = 7

10 B 5 6 = 4

11 C 3 4 = 7

	A	B	C	D	E	F
1						
2						
3						
4						
5						
6						

Symbolism

Each of these squares should contain one or more symbols from the numbered square to the left of its particular horizontal row, plus one or more symbols from the lettered square above its particular vertical column. However, one square doesn't follow this rule. Which is the odd one out?

		A	B	C	D	E	F
		◄ ≈	♣ $	‡ ¿	♦ #	♪ ¶	Σ ☼
1	∩ π	≈∩ / π	π / ∩♣	¿‡ / ∩	∩ / #♦	¶♪ / π	☼ / ∩
2	♠ ß	≈ / ♠◄	$♣ / ß	♠ / ¿ß	♦ / ß	ß / ¶♠	♠Σ / ß
3	£ ►	► / ◄≈	£ / $	► / ‡£	£# / ♦►	£♪ / ►	Σ / £
4	Ω §	≈◄ / Ω	$ / §♣	‡¿ / Ω	# / §	Ω / ♪§	§Σ / Σ
5	△ ♥	♥ / ≈△	♣ / △	♥ / △	♥ / #	♪ / ♥△	△ / Σ☼
6	▲ ♪	▲ / ◄	♪ / $▲	¿ / ♪	▲♦ / ♪	♪ / ♪▲	♪ / ☼Σ
7	▼ φ	◄ / ▼	φ / ♣	‡φ / ▼	▼ / #	φ / ♪¶	☼ / ▼

Can you place the vessels into the diagram? Some parts of vessels or sea squares have already been filled in. A number to the right or below a row or column refers to the number of occupied squares in that row or column.

Any vessel may be positioned horizontally or vertically, but no part of a vessel touches part of any other vessel, either horizontally, vertically or diagonally.

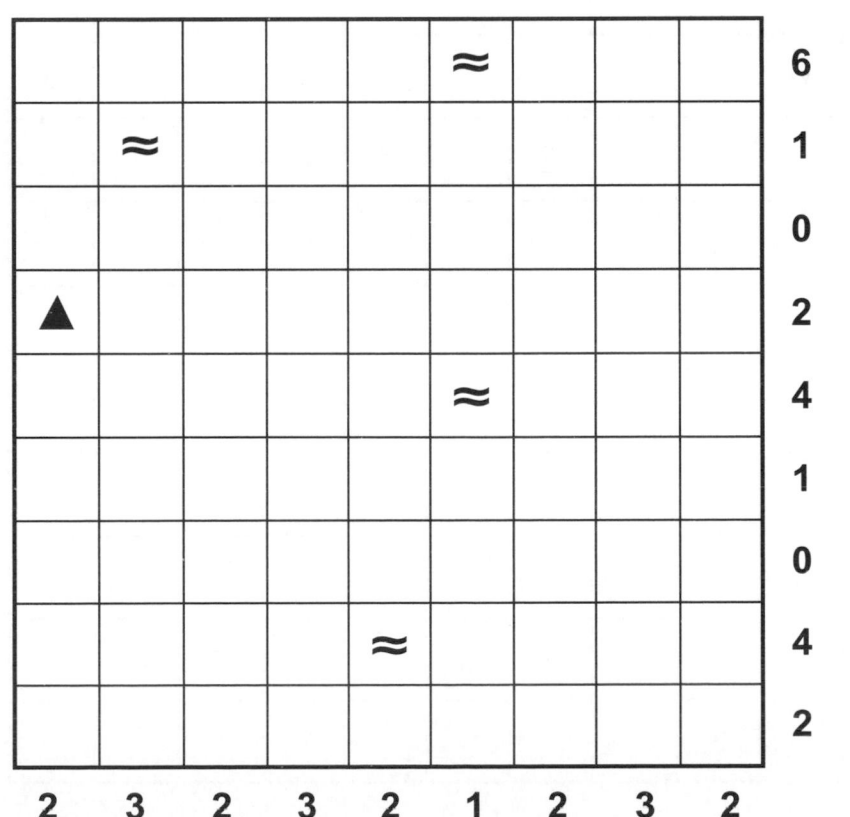

Coin Collecting

In this puzzle, an amateur coin collector has been out with his metal detector, searching for booty. He didn't have time to dig up all the coins he found, so has made a grid map, showing their locations, in the hope that if he loses the map, at least no-one else will understand it... However, he didn't count on YOU coming across the strange grid (as seen here). Will you be able to discover the correct number of coins and their precise locations?

Those squares containing numbers are empty, but where a number appears in a square, it indicates how many coins are located in the squares (up to a maximum of eight) surrounding the numbered one, touching it at any corner or side. There is only one coin in any individual square.

Place a circle into every square containing a coin.

		0			0				
0							1		0
		2		1	0				
	3								
				3		2	2		
	5		3		1				
	2	1							4
	5								
		1	3			4	4		
	3				2				

Slitherlink

Draw a single continuous loop, by connecting the dots. No line may cross the path of another.

The figure inside each set of any four surrounding dots indicates the total number of surrounding lines.

```
. . . . . . . . . . .
        3       3       3   1
. . . . . . . . . . .
  1   0       1   2   2           1
. . . . . . . . . . .
  1               2       1   3   2
. . . . . . . . . . .
              3   1   2   2       1
. . . . . . . . . . .
  1               2       2       1   2
. . . . . . . . . . .
      0       3       3   2   2
. . . . . . . . . . .
      3               1   1           2
. . . . . . . . . . .
                  2   1   1       2
. . . . . . . . . . .
      3       3   2   2       1
. . . . . . . . . . .
      0   2       1           0
. . . . . . . . . . .
      1                       3   2
. . . . . . . . . . .
      3       2   1       1   2
. . . . . . . . . . .
```

Balancing the Scales

Given that scales A and B balance perfectly, how many hearts are needed to balance scale C?

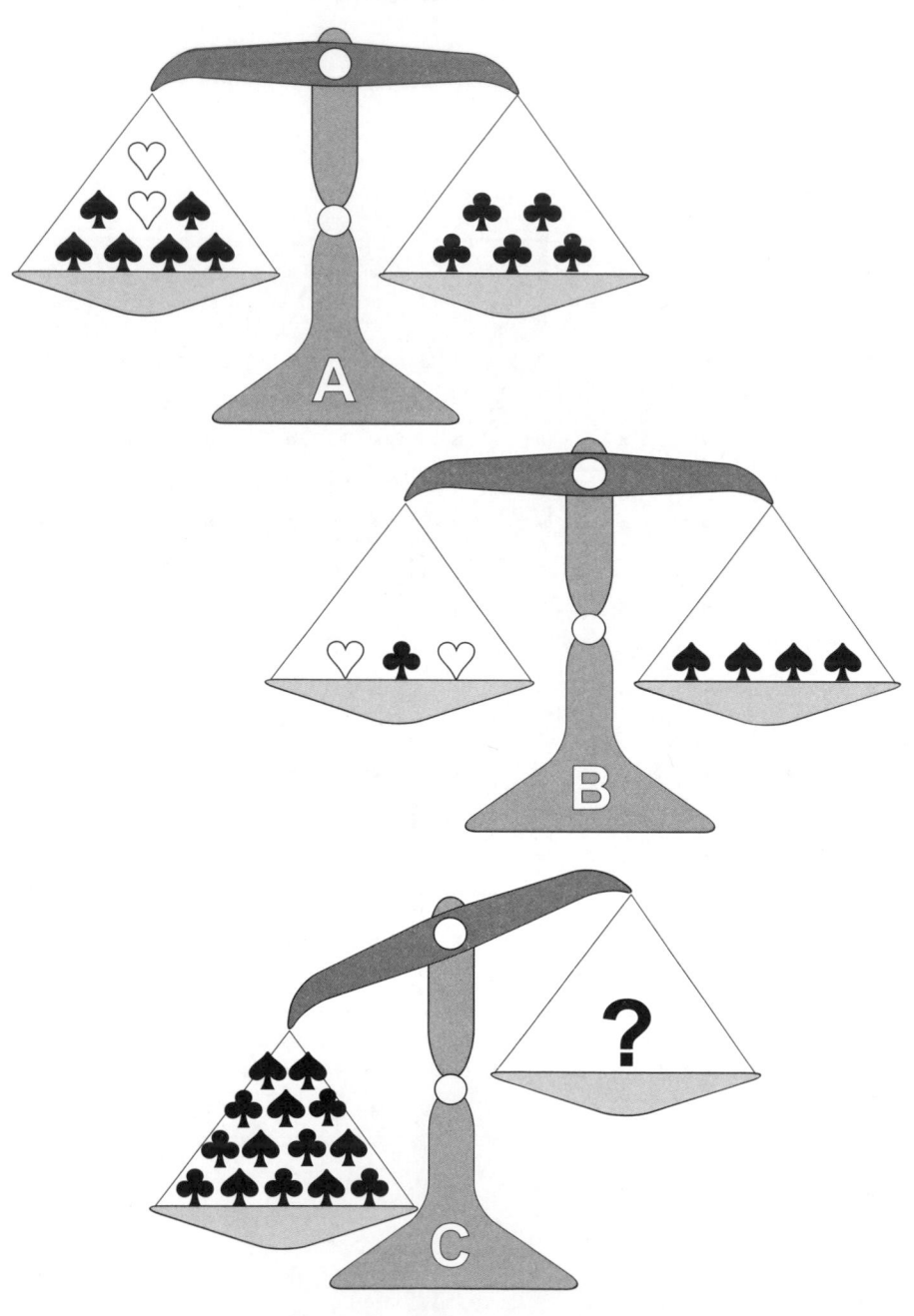

Logi-6

Every row and column of this grid should contain one each of the letters A, B, C, D, E and F. In addition, each of the six shapes (marked by thicker lines) should also contain one each of the letters A, B, C, D, E and F. Can you complete the grid?

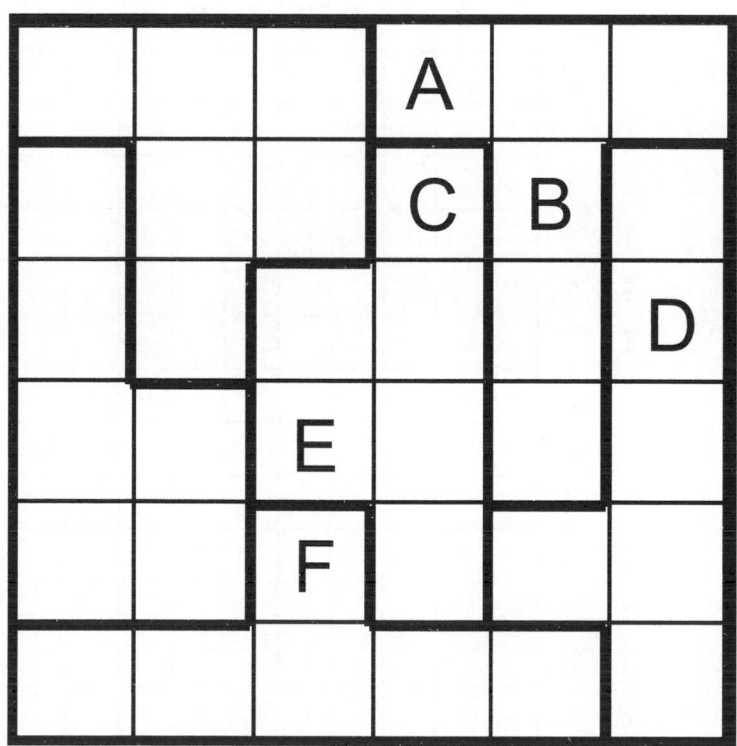

Piecework

Place all twelve of the pieces into the grid. Any may be rotated or flipped over, but none may touch another, not even diagonally. The numbers outside the grid refer to the number of consecutive black squares; and each block is separated from the others by at least one white square. For instance, '3 2' could refer to a row with none, one or more white squares, then three black squares, then at least one white square, then two more black squares, followed by any number of white squares.

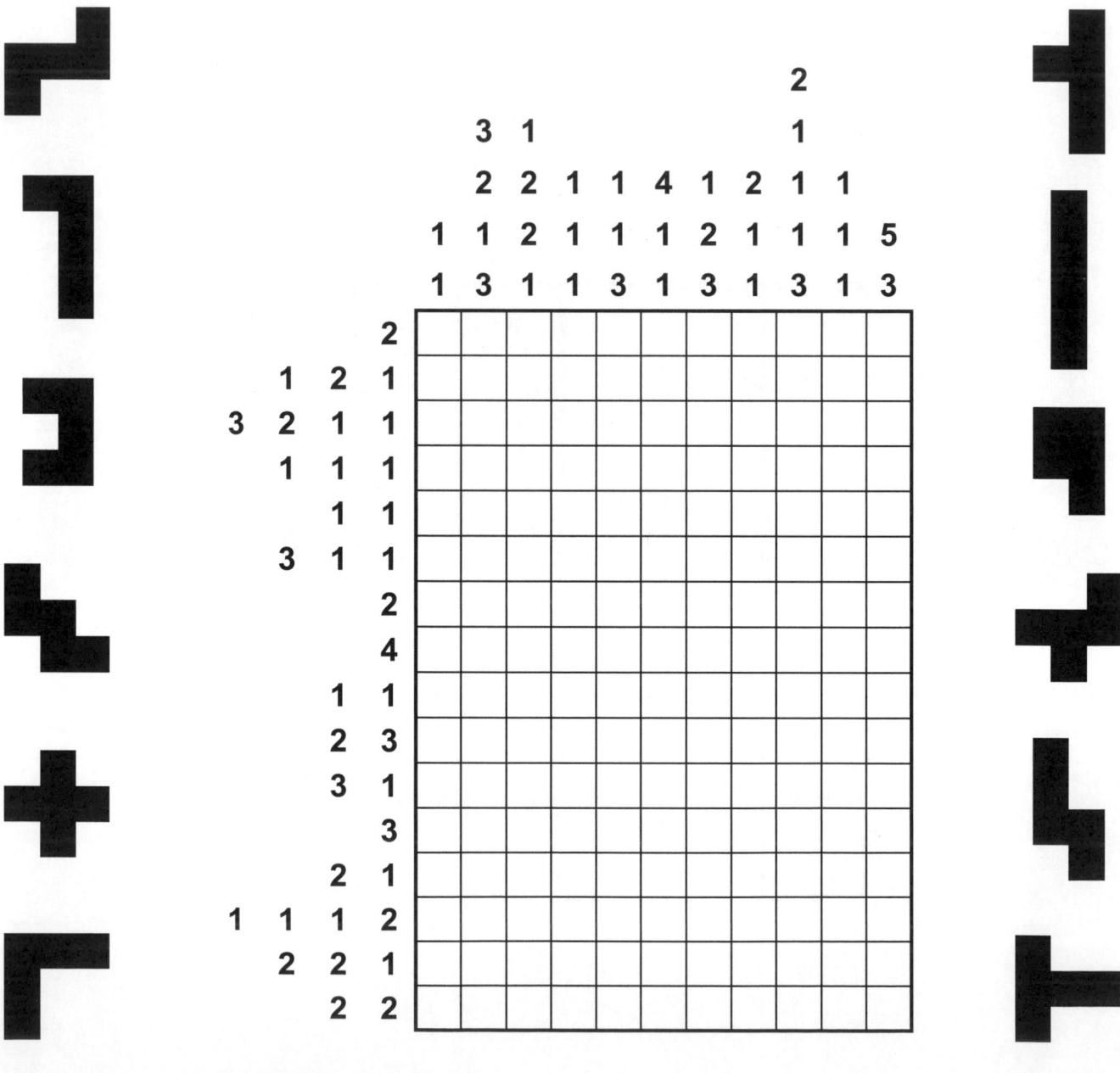

Tile Twister

Place the eight tiles into the puzzle grid so that all adjacent numbers on each tile match up. Tiles may be rotated through 360 degrees, but none may be flipped over.

2	3
4	4

2	4
2	2

2	1
2	2

3	3
4	2

				2	1
				3	1

2	1
4	4

2	3
1	3

3	2
1	4

3	1
2	2

Domino Placement

A standard set of twenty-eight dominoes has been laid out as shown. Can you draw in the edges of them all? The check-box is provided as an aid, so that you can see which dominoes have been located.

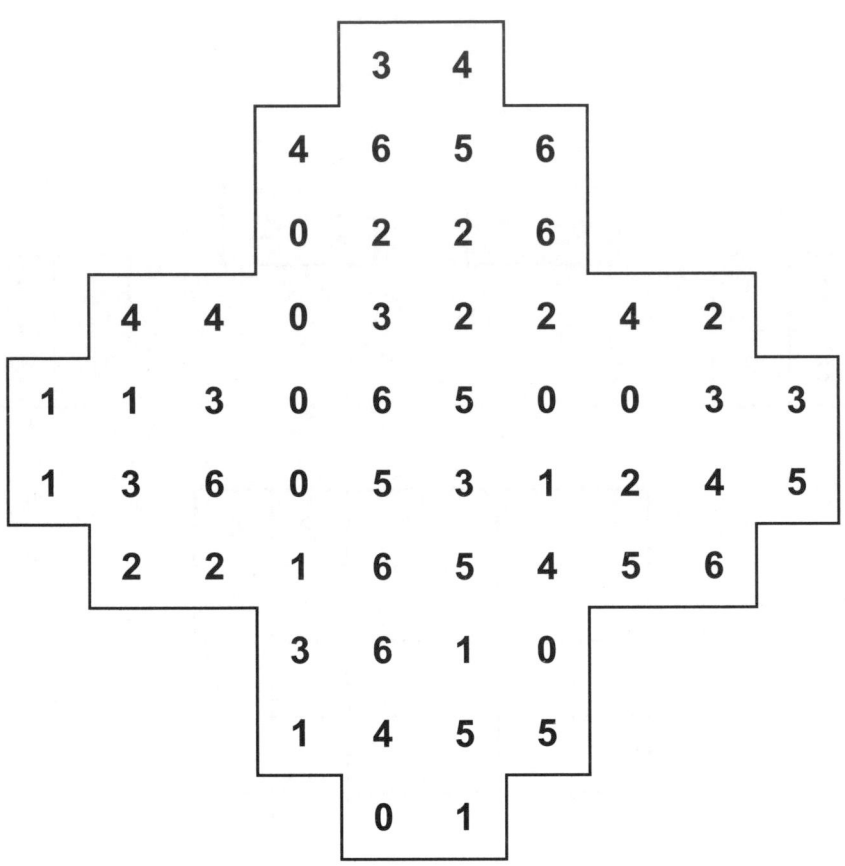

0-0	0-1	0-2	0-3	0-4	0-5	0-6	1-1	1-2	1-3	1-4	1-5	1-6	2-2

2-3	2-4	2-5	2-6	3-3	3-4	3-5	3-6	4-4	4-5	4-6	5-5	5-6	6-6

Hexagony

Can you place the hexagons into the grid, so that where any hexagon touches another along a straight line, the contents of both triangles is the same? No rotation of any hexagon is allowed!

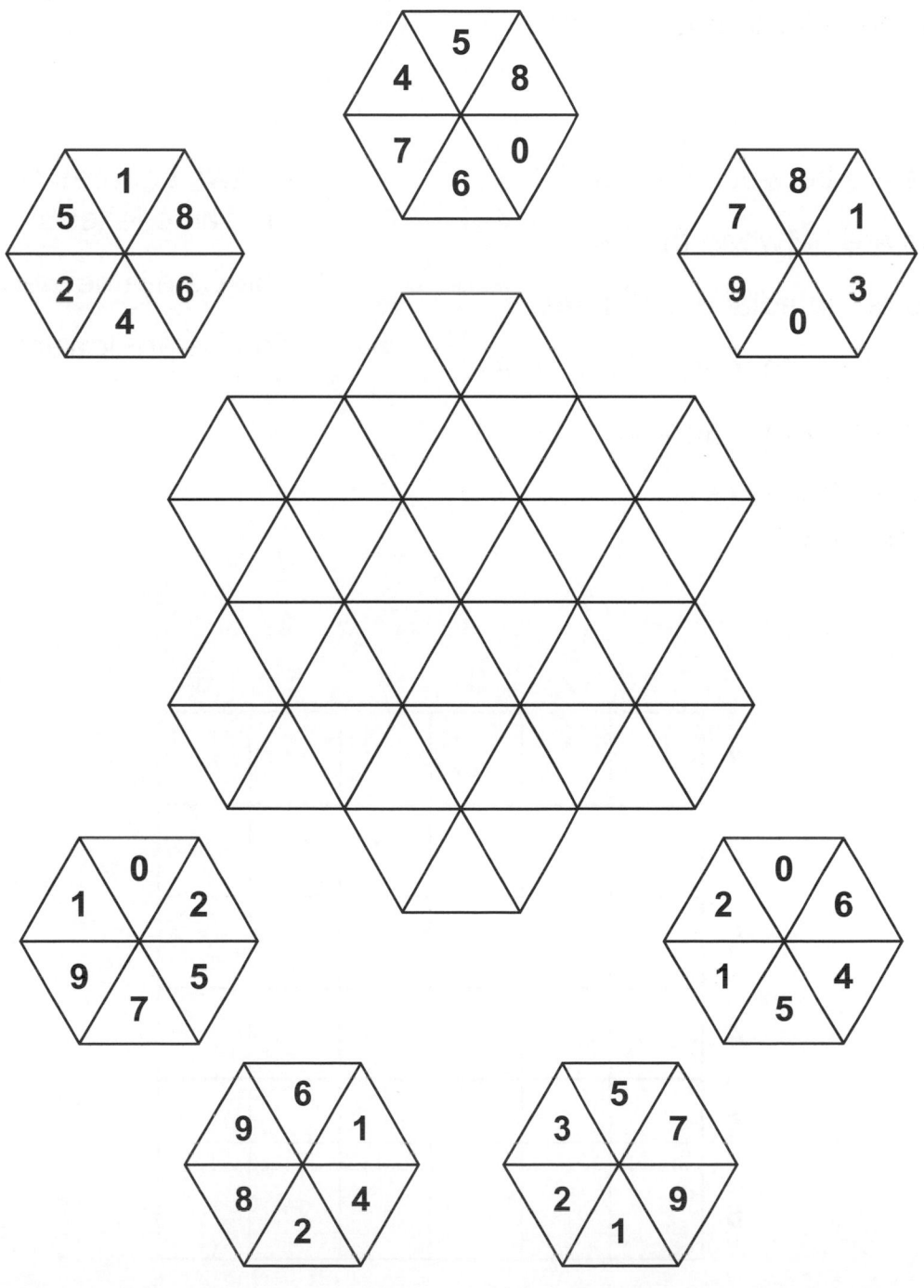

Simple as A, B, C?

Each of the small squares in the grid below contains either A, B or C. Every row, column and each of the two long diagonals has exactly two of each letter. The information in the clues refers only to the squares in that row or column. To help you solve this problem, we have provided as many clues as we think you will need! Can you tell the letter in each square?

Across

1 The As are between the Cs.

2 The Cs are between the Bs.

3 The Bs are in adjacent squares.

4 The Cs are further right than the As.

5 The Bs are further right than the As.

6 Each B is directly next to and left of a C.

Down

1 No two squares containing the same letter are adjacent.

2 The Cs are between the Bs.

6 The Bs are lower than the Cs.

	1	2	3	4	5	6
1						
2						
3						
4						
5						
6						

Total Concentration

The blank squares below should be filled with whole numbers between 1 and 40 inclusive, any of which may occur more than once, or not at all. The numbers in every horizontal row add up to the totals on the right, as do the two long diagonal lines; whilst those in every vertical column add up to the totals along the bottom. Can you discover the missing numbers?

								115

33	11	37		23		22	2	164
21	18		31		13	13	39	167
32	35	25		24	11	21	19	203
6		29	31			26	18	186
38	24	39		18	22		23	213
	3	8	15		11	10	28	131
	9	20	29	22	19			161
13	12	35	24		39	29	31	221

188	145	202	213	208	152	150	188	179

Shape Up

Every row and column in this grid originally contained one circle, one diamond, one square, one triangle and two blank squares, although not necessarily in that order.

Every symbol with a black arrow refers to the first of the four symbols encountered when travelling in the direction of the arrow. Every symbol with a white arrow refers to the second of the four symbols encountered in the direction of the arrow. Can you complete the original grid?

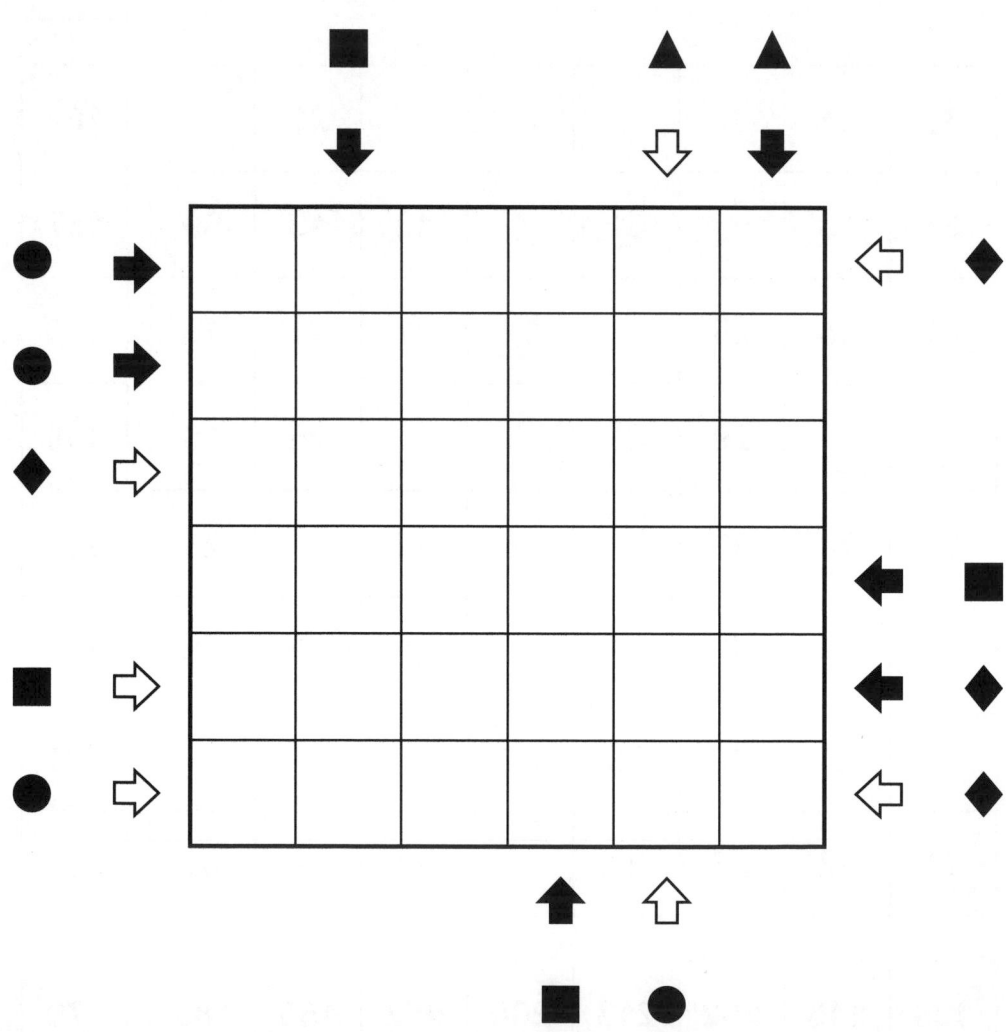

Given that the letters are valued 1-26 according to their places in the alphabet, can you crack the mystery code to reveal the missing letter?

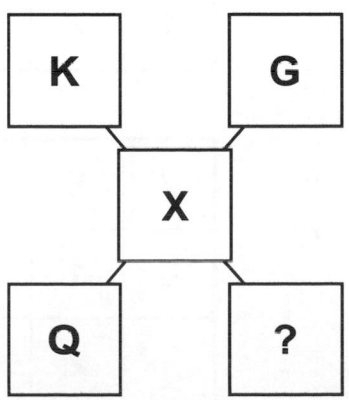

Whatever Next?

Which of the four lettered alternatives (A, B, C or D) fits most logically into the empty square?

1

5	3	6
1	7	4
2	5	3

2

6	1	7
4	2	5
3	6	1

3

7	4	2
5	3	6
1	7	4

4

?	

A

7	4	2
5	3	6
1	7	4

B

3	6	1
7	4	2
5	3	6

C

2	5	3
6	1	7
4	2	5

D

1	7	4
2	5	3
6	1	7

The Bottom Line

Can you fill each square in the bottom line with the correct digit? Every square in the solution contains only one digit from each of the lettered lines above, although two or more squares in the solution may contain the same digit.

At the end of every row is a score, which shows:

  a   the number of digits placed in the correct finishing position on the bottom line, as indicated by a tick; and

  b   the number of digits which appear on the bottom line, but in a different position, as indicated by a cross.

SCORE

A	1	2	3	4	✗ ✗
B	3	5	4	6	✗ ✗
C	5	4	2	7	✗ ✗
D	2	8	1	3	✗ ✗
E	1	4	6	8	✓ ✗
					✓✓✓✓

Combiku

Each horizontal row and vertical column should contain different shapes and different numbers.

Every square will contain one number and one shape and no combination may be repeated anywhere else in the puzzle; so, for instance, if a square contains a 3 and a star, then no other square containing a 3 will also contain a star and no other square with a star will contain a 3.

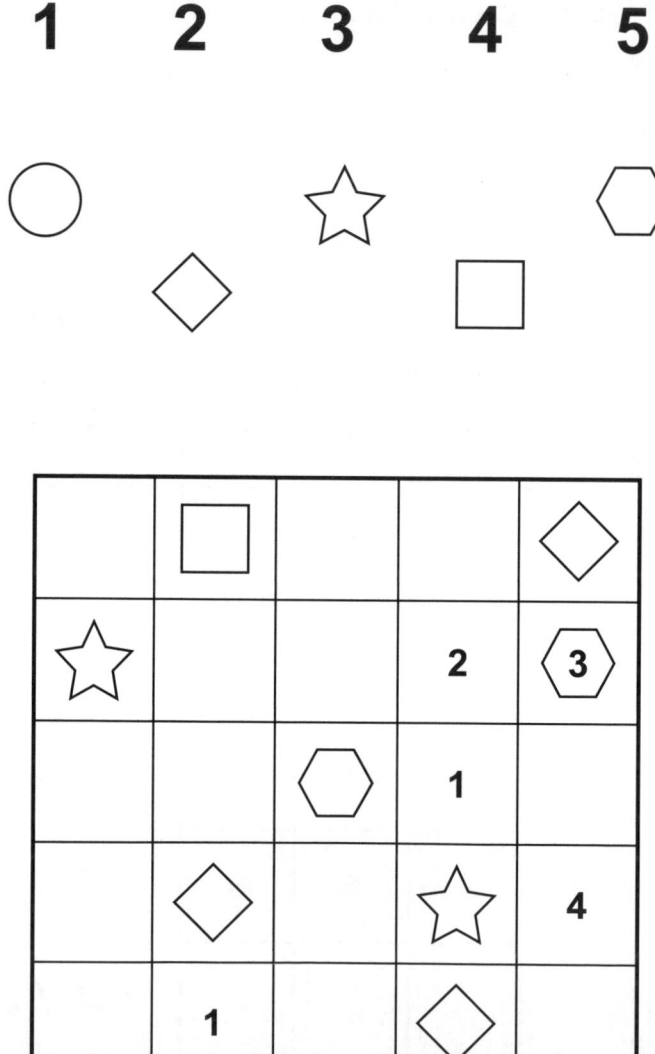

Twelve L-shapes like the ones here need to be inserted in the grid and each L has one hole in it. There are three pieces of each of the four kinds shown here and any piece may be turned or flipped over before being put in the grid. No pieces of the same kind touch, even at a corner.

The pieces fit together so well that you cannot see any spaces between them; only the holes show. Can you tell where the Ls are?

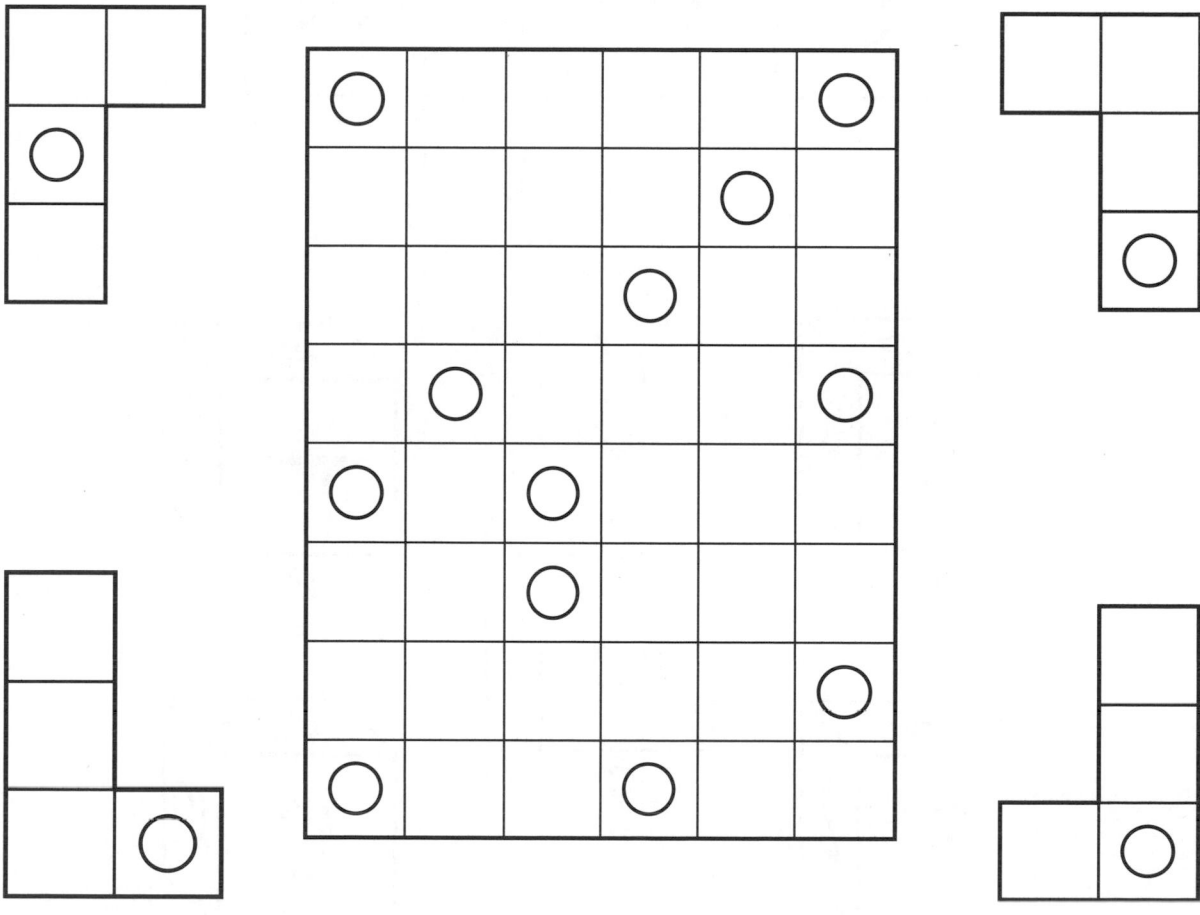

Box Clever

When the box below is folded to form a cube, just one of the five options (A, B, C, D or E) can be produced. Which?

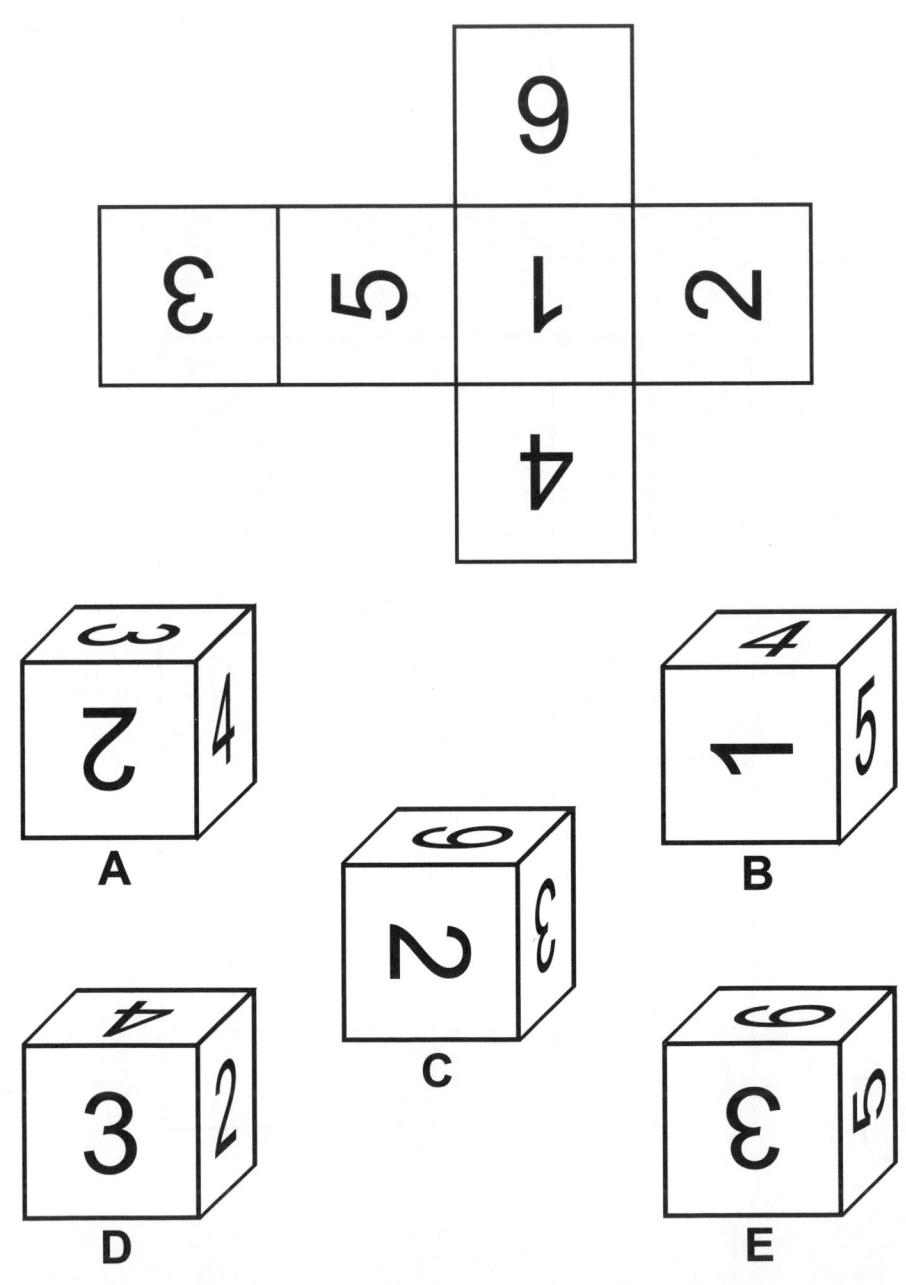

Latin Square

The grid should be filled with numbers from 1 to 6, so that each number appears just once in every row and column. The clues refer to the digit totals in the squares, for example A 1 2 3 = 6 means that the numbers in squares A1, A2 and A3 add up to 6.

1 D E F 5 = 10

2 A B C 6 = 12

3 A 3 4 = 4

4 B 1 2 = 11

5 C 4 5 = 10

6 D 1 2 = 7

7 E 3 4 = 8

8 F 3 4 = 7

9 E F 1 = 4

10 E F 2 = 7

11 C D 3 = 11

	A	B	C	D	E	F
1						
2						
3						
4						
5						
6						

Symbolism

Each of these squares should contain one or more symbols from the numbered square to the left of its particular horizontal row, plus one or more symbols from the lettered square above its particular vertical column. However, one square doesn't follow this rule. Which is the odd one out?

		A	B	C	D	E	F
		◄ ≈	♣ $	‡ ¿	♦ #	♪ ¶	Σ ☼
1	∩ π	∩ ≈ ◄	♣ π ∩	‡ ¿ π	# ∩ ♦	∩ π ¶	☼ π
2	♠ ß	≈ ß ◄	♣ $ ♠	‡ ♠ ¿	# ß ♠	♠ ß ♪	ß Σ ♠
3	£ ▶	▶ ≈ ◄	♣ £	£ ¿	♦ ▶ #	£ ▶ ¶	☼ ▶
4	Ω §	≈ § ◄	♣ § Ω	§ ‡	Ω § ♦	¶ Ω	Ω Σ
5	Δ ♥	Δ ♥ ≈	Δ ♣	¿ ‡ ♥	# ♦ ♥	♪ ♥	Δ Σ ☼
6	▲ ♫	▲ ♫ ≈	$ ♣	‡ ♫ ▲	# ▲	♫ ♪	▲ Σ
7	▼ φ	◄ ▼	♣ φ ▼	φ ‡	▼ ♦ #	φ ¶	▼ ☼

Battleships

Can you place the vessels into the diagram? Some parts of vessels or sea squares have already been filled in. A number to the right or below a row or column refers to the number of occupied squares in that row or column.

Any vessel may be positioned horizontally or vertically, but no part of a vessel touches part of any other vessel, either horizontally, vertically or diagonally.

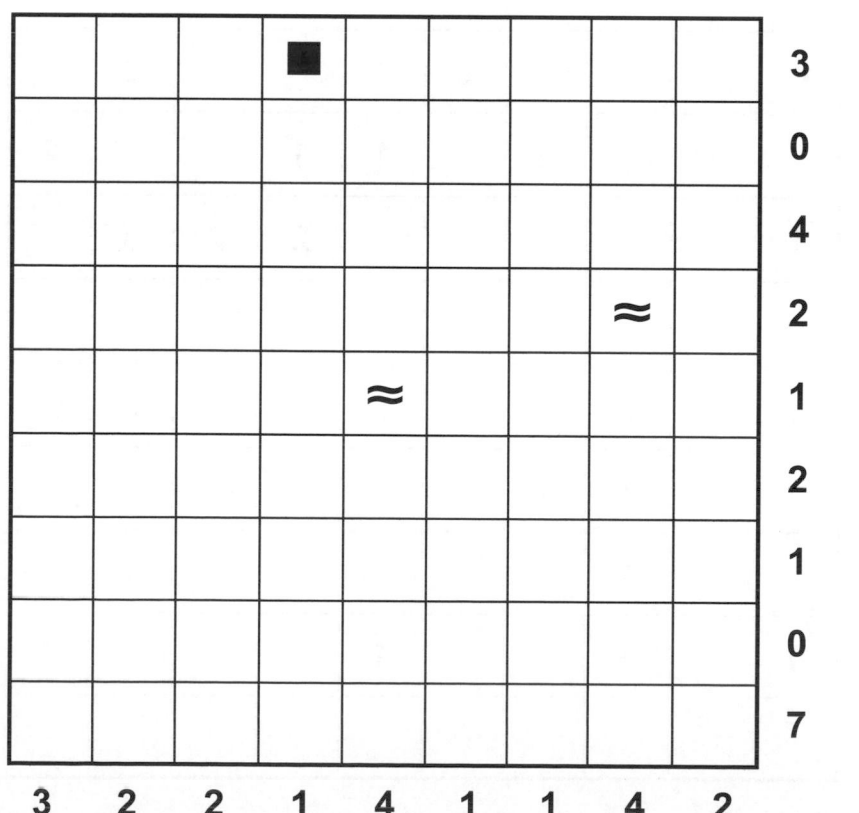

Coin Collecting

In this puzzle, an amateur coin collector has been out with his metal detector, searching for booty. He didn't have time to dig up all the coins he found, so has made a grid map, showing their locations, in the hope that if he loses the map, at least no-one else will understand it... However, he didn't count on YOU coming across the strange grid (as seen here). Will you be able to discover the correct number of coins and their precise locations?

Those squares containing numbers are empty, but where a number appears in a square, it indicates how many coins are located in the squares (up to a maximum of eight) surrounding the numbered one, touching it at any corner or side. There is only one coin in any individual square.

Place a circle into every square containing a coin.

	3					1			
			4	2	1		1	2	
	2		2		1	1			2
1						2	2	3	
				3					
1		3			3	1		2	2
		1	2				2		1
		1						1	
4		3			1				1
			0			1			

Slitherlink

Draw a single continuous loop, by connecting the dots. No line may cross the path of another.

The figure inside each set of any four surrounding dots indicates the total number of surrounding lines.

Balancing the Scales

Given that scales A and B balance perfectly, how many spades are needed to balance scale C?

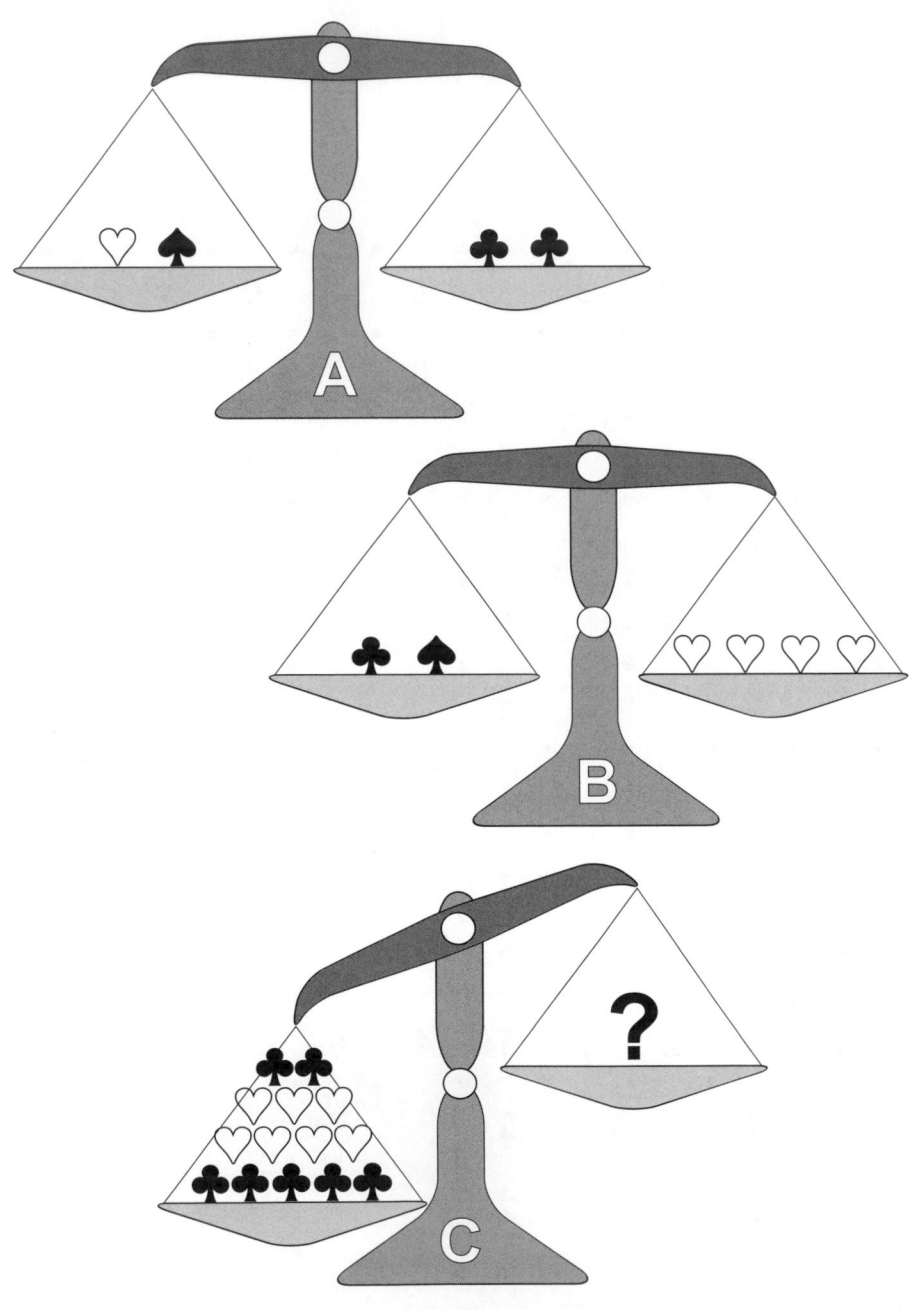

Logi-6

Every row and column of this grid should contain one each of the letters A, B, C, D, E and F. In addition, each of the six shapes (marked by thicker lines) should also contain one each of the letters A, B, C, D, E and F. Can you complete the grid?

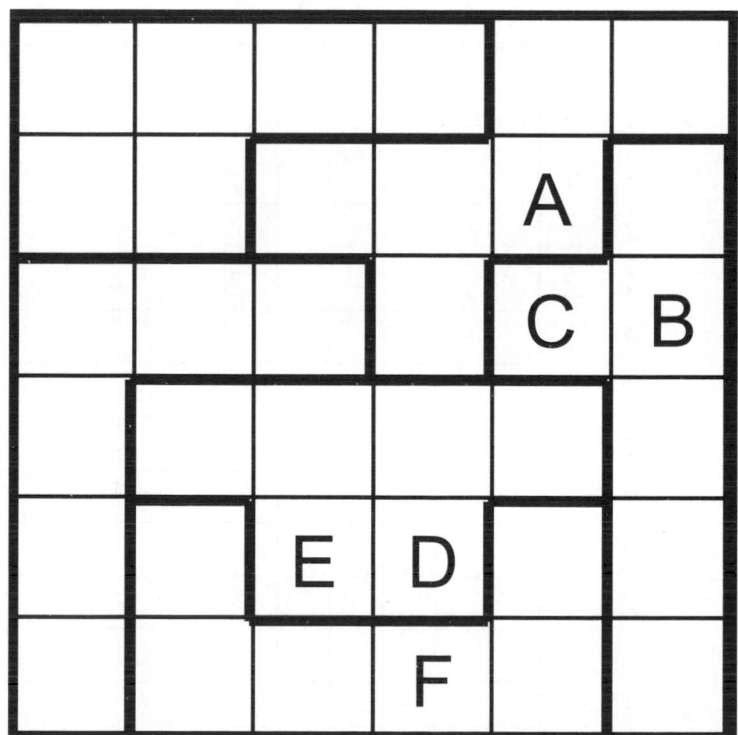

Piecework

Place all twelve of the pieces into the grid. Any may be rotated or flipped over, but none may touch another, not even diagonally. The numbers outside the grid refer to the number of consecutive black squares; and each block is separated from the others by at least one white square. For instance, '3 2' could refer to a row with none, one or more white squares, then three black squares, then at least one white square, then two more black squares, followed by any number of white squares.

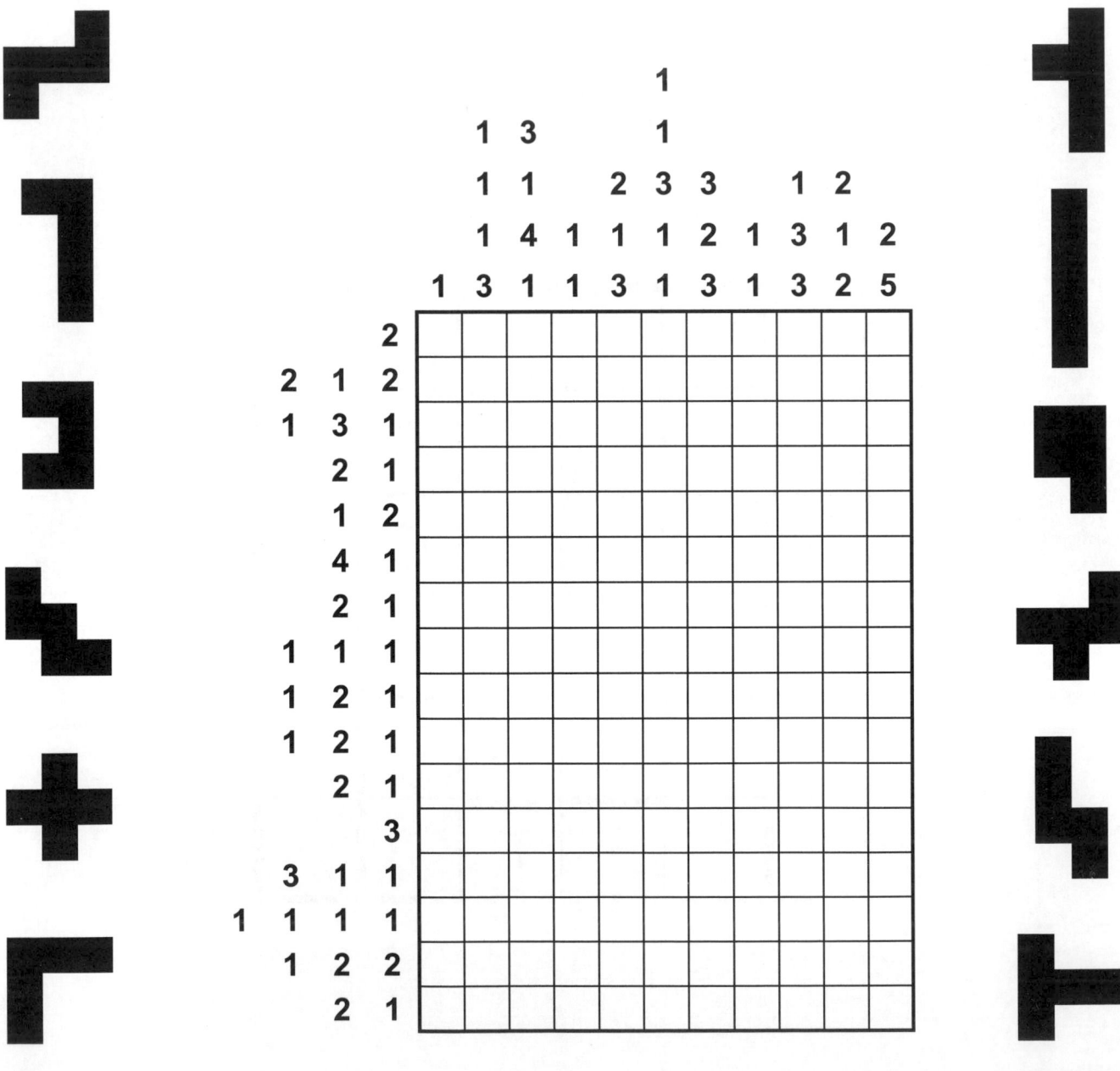

Tile Twister

Place the eight tiles into the puzzle grid so that all adjacent numbers on each tile match up. Tiles may be rotated through 360 degrees, but none may be flipped over.

1	2
3	4

3	2
2	3

3	3
4	2

1	3
2	4

1	3				
3	2				

1	4
1	2

4	1
3	2

3	1
3	4

1	1
2	3

Domino Placement

A standard set of twenty-eight dominoes has been laid out as shown. Can you draw in the edges of them all? The check-box is provided as an aid, so that you can see which dominoes have been located.

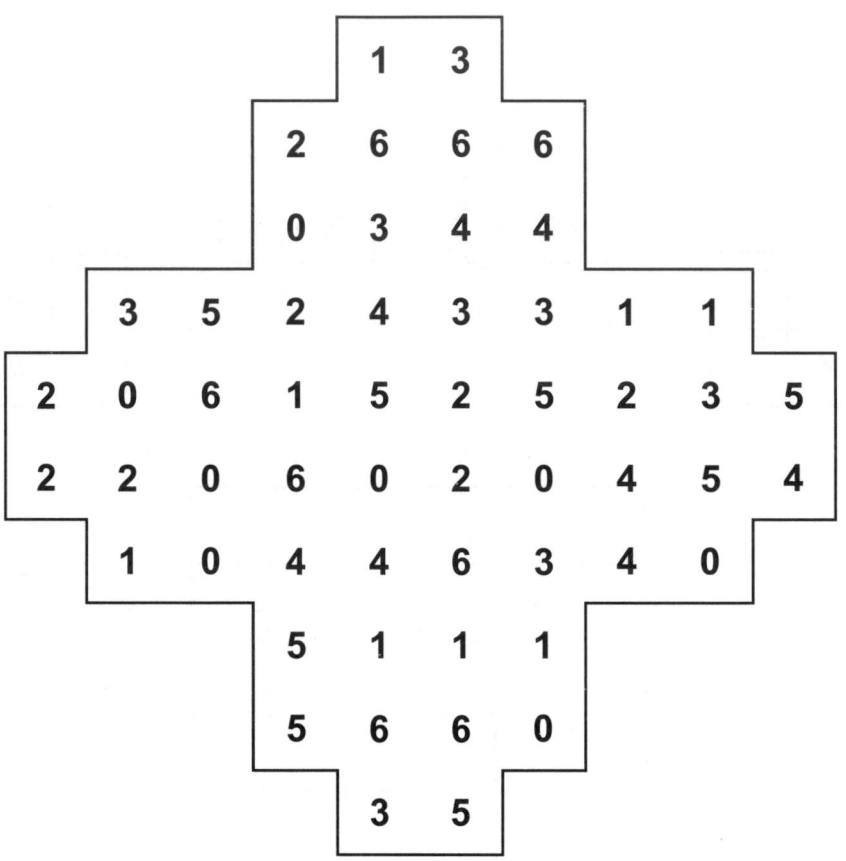

0-0	0-1	0-2	0-3	0-4	0-5	0-6	1-1	1-2	1-3	1-4	1-5	1-6	2-2

2-3	2-4	2-5	2-6	3-3	3-4	3-5	3-6	4-4	4-5	4-6	5-5	5-6	6-6

Hexagony

Can you place the hexagons into the grid, so that where any hexagon touches another along a straight line, the contents of both triangles is the same? No rotation of any hexagon is allowed!

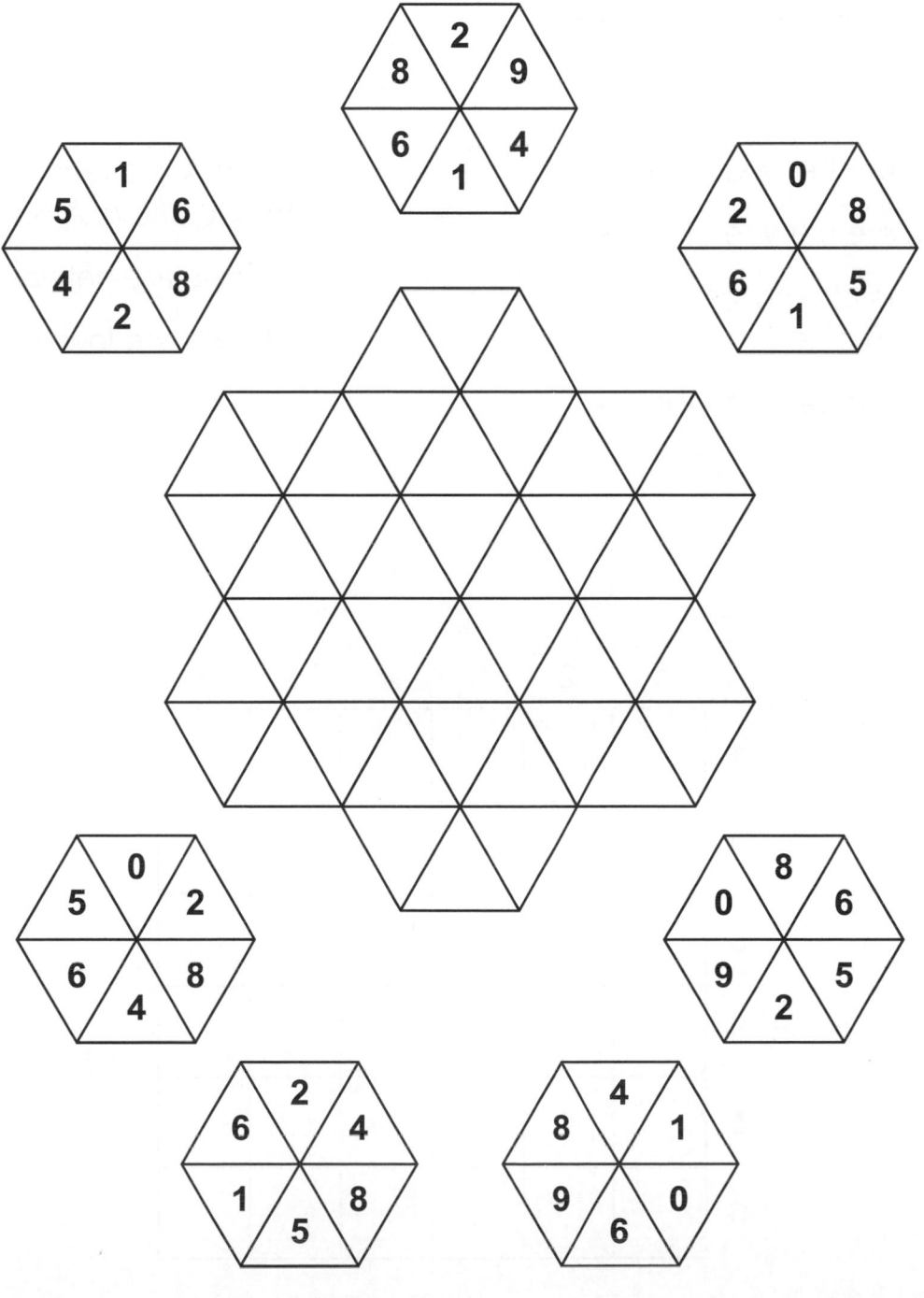

Simple as A, B, C?

Each of the small squares in the grid below contains either A, B or C. Every row, column and each of the two long diagonals has exactly two of each letter. The information in the clues refers only to the squares in that row or column. To help you solve this problem, we have provided as many clues as we think you will need! Can you tell the letter in each square?

Across

1 The As are between the Bs.

4 The Bs are between the Cs.

5 Each A is directly next to and left of a C.

6 The Bs are between the As.

Down

1 Each A is directly next to and above a B.

5 The As are between the Bs.

6 The As are lower than the Cs.

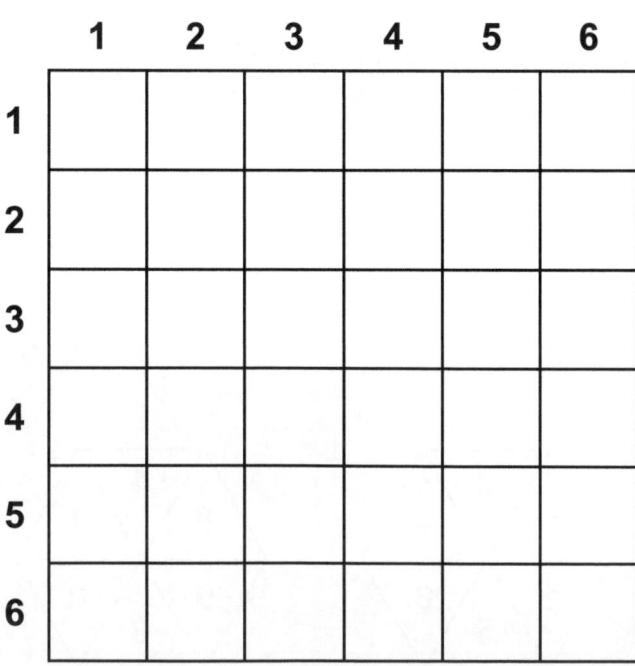

Total Concentration

The blank squares below should be filled with whole numbers between 1 and 40 inclusive, any of which may occur more than once, or not at all. The numbers in every horizontal row add up to the totals on the right, as do the two long diagonal lines; whilst those in every vertical column add up to the totals along the bottom. Can you discover the missing numbers?

								172
22	9	40	37	37		34	7	195
39	2	31	18			36	8	207
38	39	8	8		30	30	19	174
	22	10		7	7		16	158
24		1	38	38		27		173
	31		9	12	21	40		160
		16	27	25	39	2	18	171
38	7	35		12		20	31	175
232	153	143	172	169	173	223	148	151

Shape Up

Every row and column in this grid originally contained one circle, one diamond, one square, one triangle and two blank squares, although not necessarily in that order.

Every symbol with a black arrow refers to the first of the four symbols encountered when travelling in the direction of the arrow. Every symbol with a white arrow refers to the second of the four symbols encountered in the direction of the arrow. Can you complete the original grid?

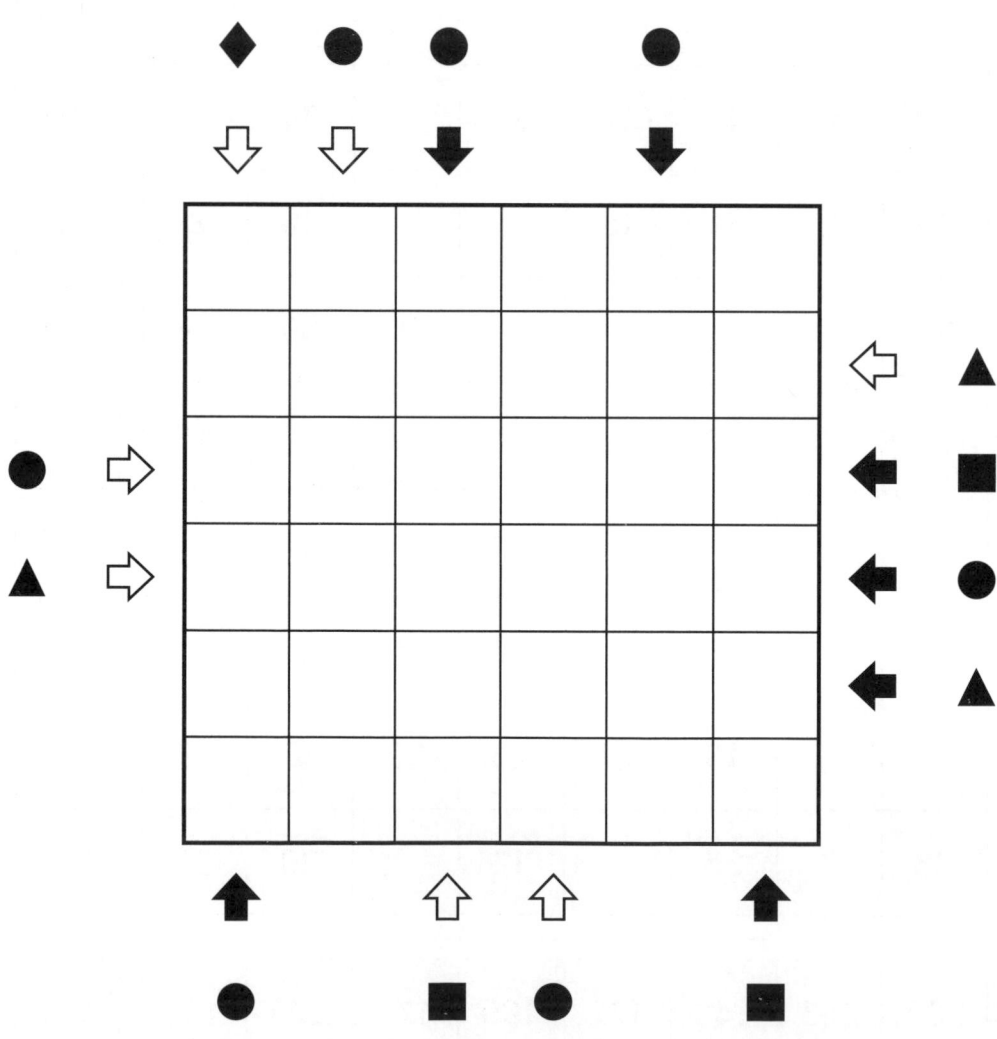

Mind Over Matter

Given that the letters are valued 1-26 according to their places in the alphabet, can you crack the mystery code to reveal the missing letter?

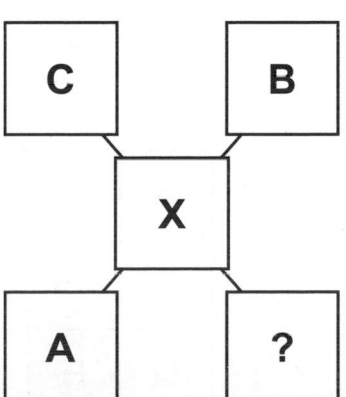

Whatever Next?

Which of the four lettered alternatives (A, B, C or D) fits most logically into the empty square?

1

S	G	K
A	19	E
M	W	Q

2

M	Q	E
C	13	K
A	G	S

3

E	G	Q
K	31	W
S	C	A

4

	?	

~~~~~~

A

A	M	W
C	11	Q
G	E	S

B

S	A	W
E	27	C
M	Q	G

C

A	M	G
E	15	S
Q	H	C

D

G	K	W
I	23	C
A	E	H

The Bottom Line

Can you fill each square in the bottom line with the correct digit? Every square in the solution contains only one digit from each of the lettered lines above, although two or more squares in the solution may contain the same digit.

At the end of every row is a score, which shows:

a the number of digits placed in the correct finishing position on the bottom line, as indicated by a tick; and

b the number of digits which appear on the bottom line, but in a different position, as indicated by a cross.

SCORE

A	1	2	3	4	✗
B	4	1	1	5	✗
C	2	3	6	6	✗
D	5	7	8	8	✗
E	7	4	7	3	✓
					✓✓✓✓

Combiku

Each horizontal row and vertical column should contain different shapes and different numbers.

Every square will contain one number and one shape and no combination may be repeated anywhere else in the puzzle; so, for instance, if a square contains a 3 and a star, then no other square containing a 3 will also contain a star and no other square with a star will contain a 3.

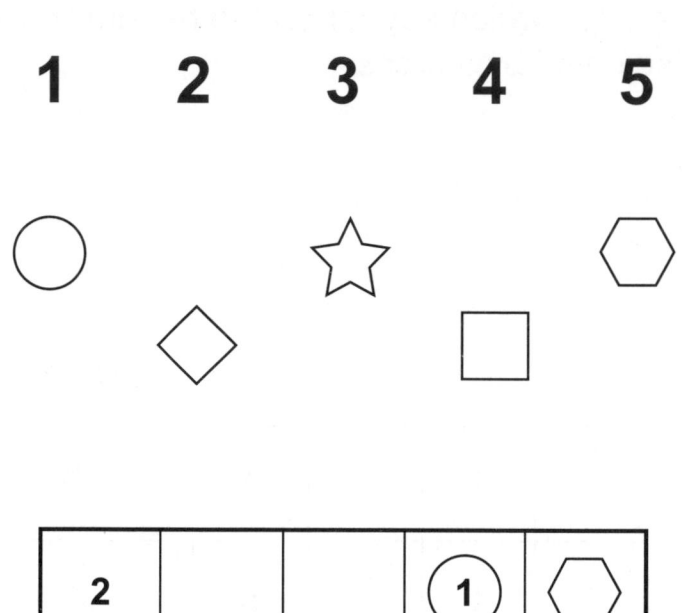

Twelve L-shapes like the ones here need to be inserted in the grid and each L has one hole in it. There are three pieces of each of the four kinds shown here and any piece may be turned or flipped over before being put in the grid. No pieces of the same kind touch, even at a corner.

The pieces fit together so well that you cannot see any spaces between them; only the holes show. Can you tell where the Ls are?

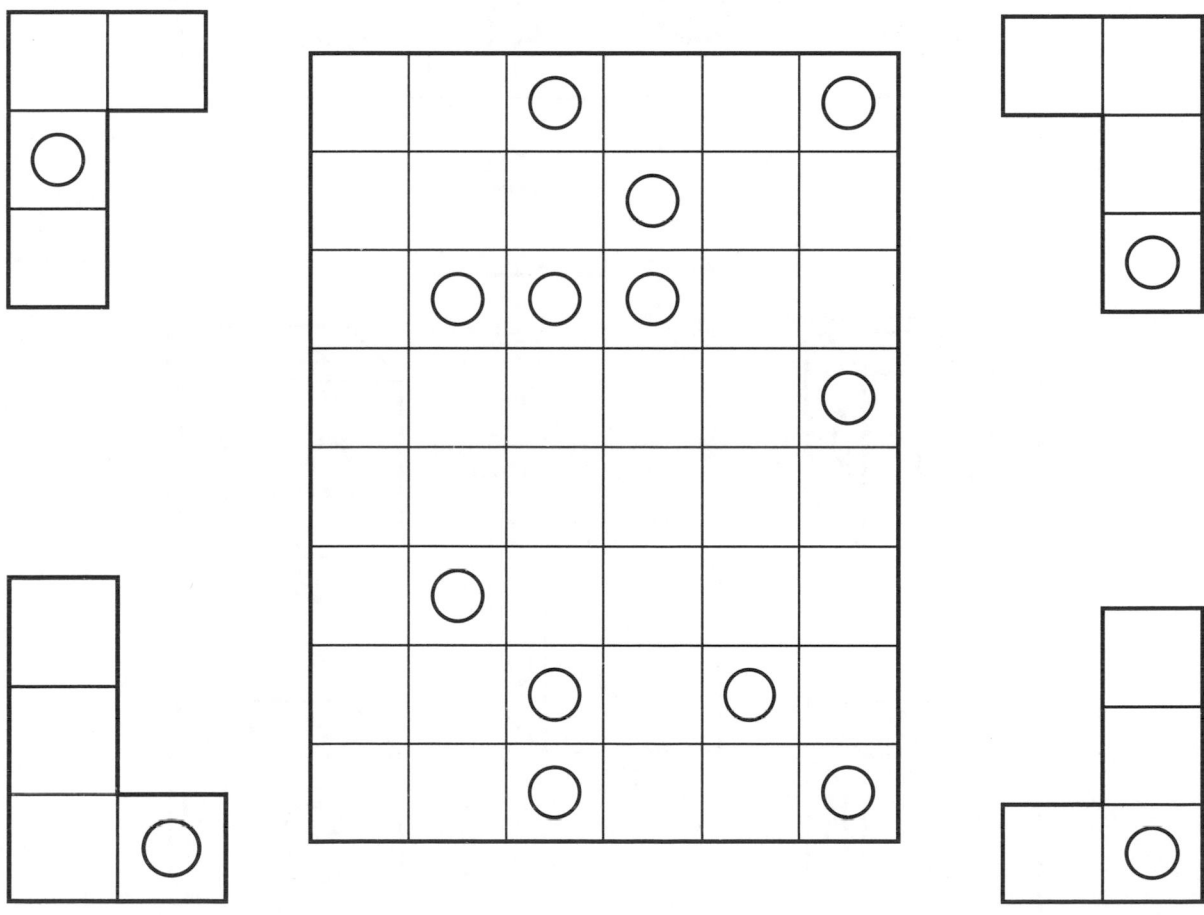

Box Clever

When the box below is folded to form a cube, just one of the five options (A, B, C, D or E) can be produced. Which?

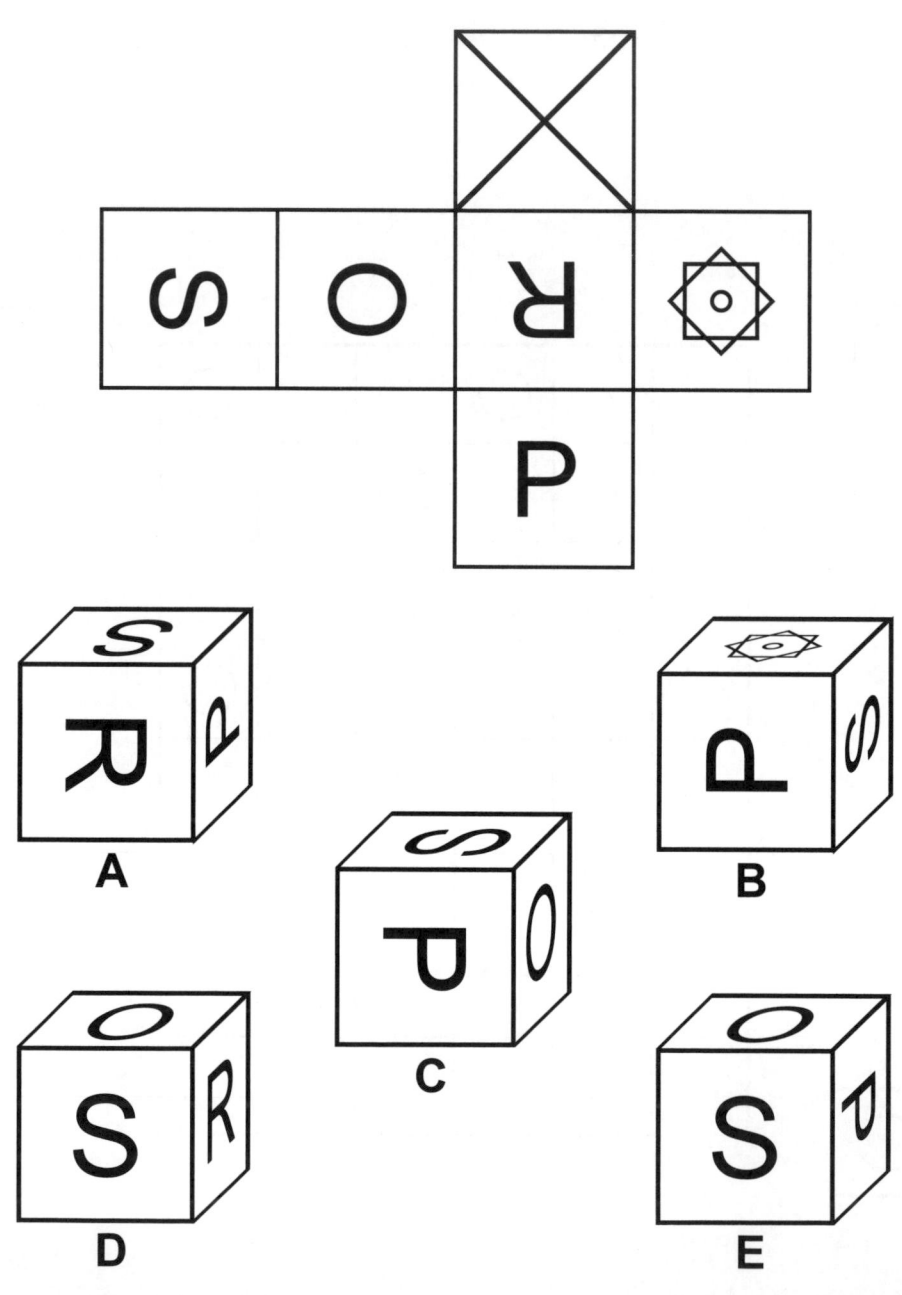

Latin Square

The grid should be filled with numbers from 1 to 6, so that each number appears just once in every row and column. The clues refer to the digit totals in the squares, for example A 1 2 3 = 6 means that the numbers in squares A1, A2 and A3 add up to 6.

1 B 4 5 = 6

2 C 2 3 = 8

3 D 1 2 = 3

4 E 4 5 6 = 10

5 F 5 6 = 6

6 E F 1 = 10

7 E F 2 = 8

8 D E 3 = 4

9 C D 4 = 11

10 C D 5 = 10

11 A B C 6 = 9

	A	B	C	D	E	F
1						
2						
3						
4						
5						
6						

Symbolism

Each of these squares should contain one or more symbols from the numbered square to the left of its particular horizontal row, plus one or more symbols from the lettered square above its particular vertical column. However, one square doesn't follow this rule. Which is the odd one out?

	A (◄ ≈)	B (♣ $)	C (‡ ¿)	D (♦ #)	E (♪ ¶)	F (Σ ☼)
1 (∩ π)	π ∩ ≈	$ ∩	‡ π ¿	∩ π ♦	¶ π ♪	☼ Σ ∩
2 (♠ ß)	♠ ◄	♣ ß ♠	ß ¿	♦ ♠ #	¶ ♪ ß	♠ ☼
3 (£ ►)	£ ≈	$ £	► ‡	# ► ♦	► £ ¶	► Σ £
4 (Ω §)	◄ Ω ≈	§ ♣	¿ Ω ‡	♦ Ω §	§ ♪	☼ Ω
5 (△ ♥)	◄ ♥ △	♥ $	△ ¿	♥ #	♪ ♥	△ ☼
6 (▲ ♫)	≈ ▲ ♫	▲ $	‡ ♫	# ▲	♫ ¶	♫ ▲ ☼
7 (▼ φ)	◄ φ	▼ $ ♣	φ ‡	φ ♦	▼ ♪	Σ ☼

Battleships

Can you place the vessels into the diagram? Some parts of vessels or sea squares have already been filled in. A number to the right or below a row or column refers to the number of occupied squares in that row or column.

Any vessel may be positioned horizontally or vertically, but no part of a vessel touches part of any other vessel, either horizontally, vertically or diagonally.

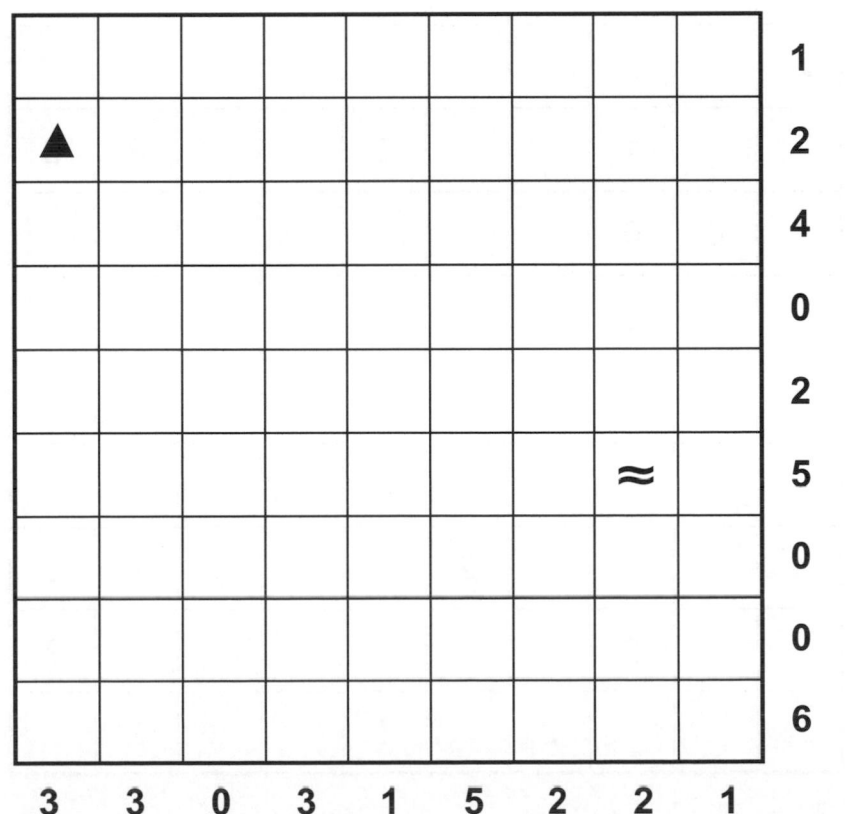

Coin Collecting

In this puzzle, an amateur coin collector has been out with his metal detector, searching for booty. He didn't have time to dig up all the coins he found, so has made a grid map, showing their locations, in the hope that if he loses the map, at least no-one else will understand it... However, he didn't count on YOU coming across the strange grid (as seen here). Will you be able to discover the correct number of coins and their precise locations?

Those squares containing numbers are empty, but where a number appears in a square, it indicates how many coins are located in the squares (up to a maximum of eight) surrounding the numbered one, touching it at any corner or side. There is only one coin in any individual square.

Place a circle into every square containing a coin.

	3		3	2	1				1
								2	
		1			5			3	3
	0	0							
		1			2		1		
2			1					1	
					0	1			
4				2			3		2
		3							2
3			2		1			2	

Slitherlink

Draw a single continuous loop, by connecting the dots. No line may cross the path of another.

The figure inside each set of any four surrounding dots indicates the total number of surrounding lines.

Balancing the Scales

Given that scales A and B balance perfectly, how many diamonds are needed to balance scale C?

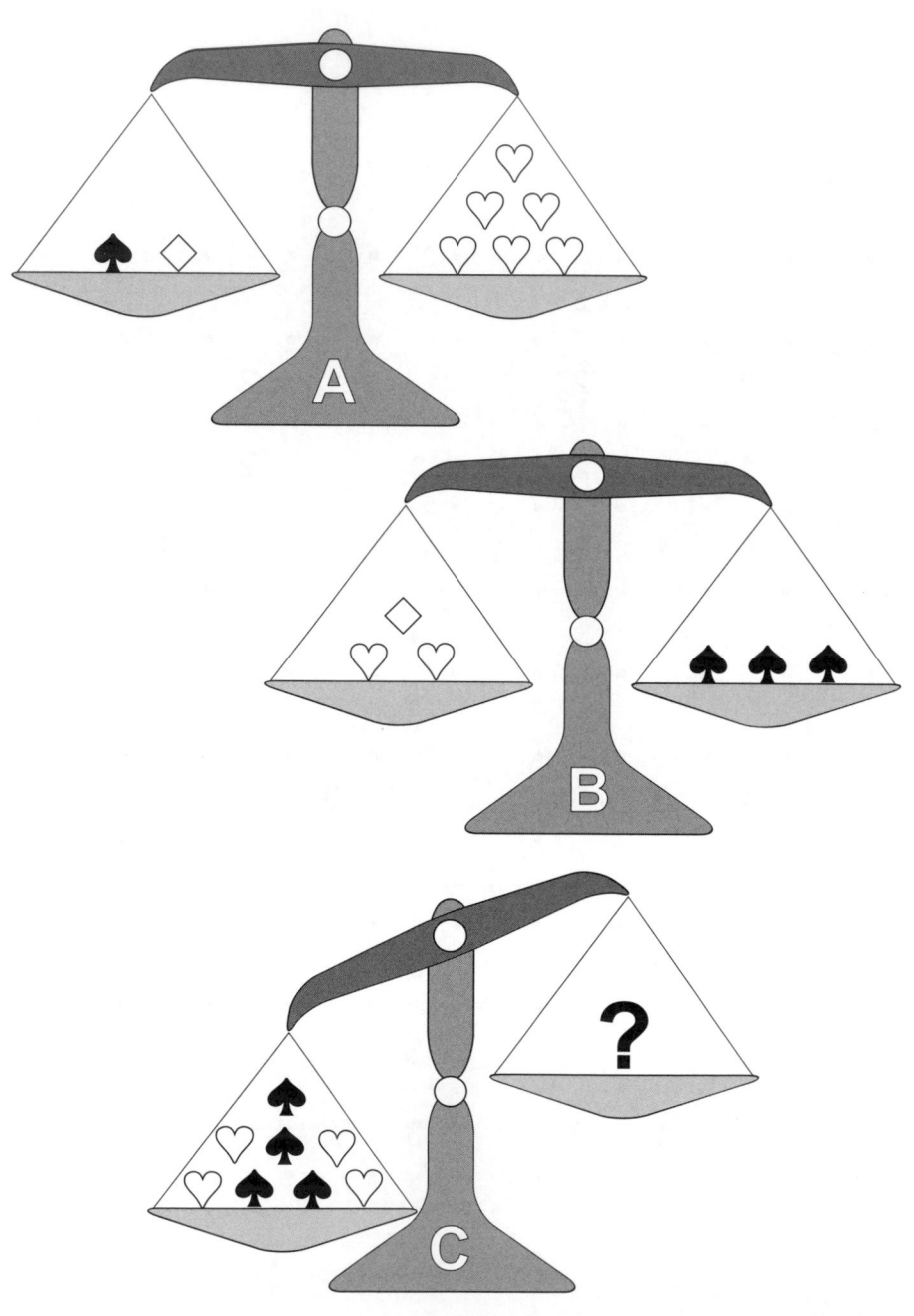

Every row and column of this grid should contain one each of the letters A, B, C, D, E and F. In addition, each of the six shapes (marked by thicker lines) should also contain one each of the letters A, B, C, D, E and F. Can you complete the grid?

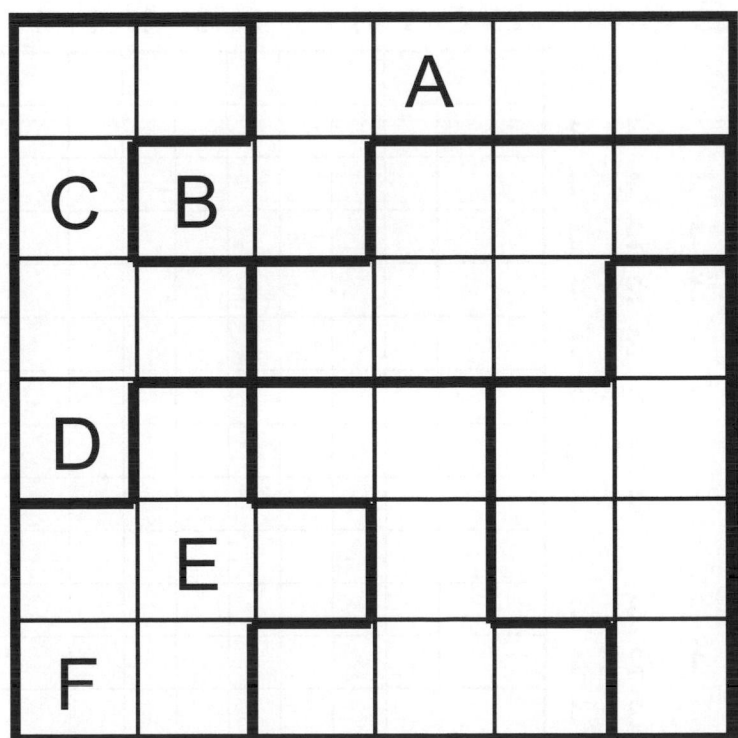

Piecework

Place all twelve of the pieces into the grid. Any may be rotated or flipped over, but none may touch another, not even diagonally. The numbers outside the grid refer to the number of consecutive black squares; and each block is separated from the others by at least one white square. For instance, '3 2' could refer to a row with none, one or more white squares, then three black squares, then at least one white square, then two more black squares, followed by any number of white squares.

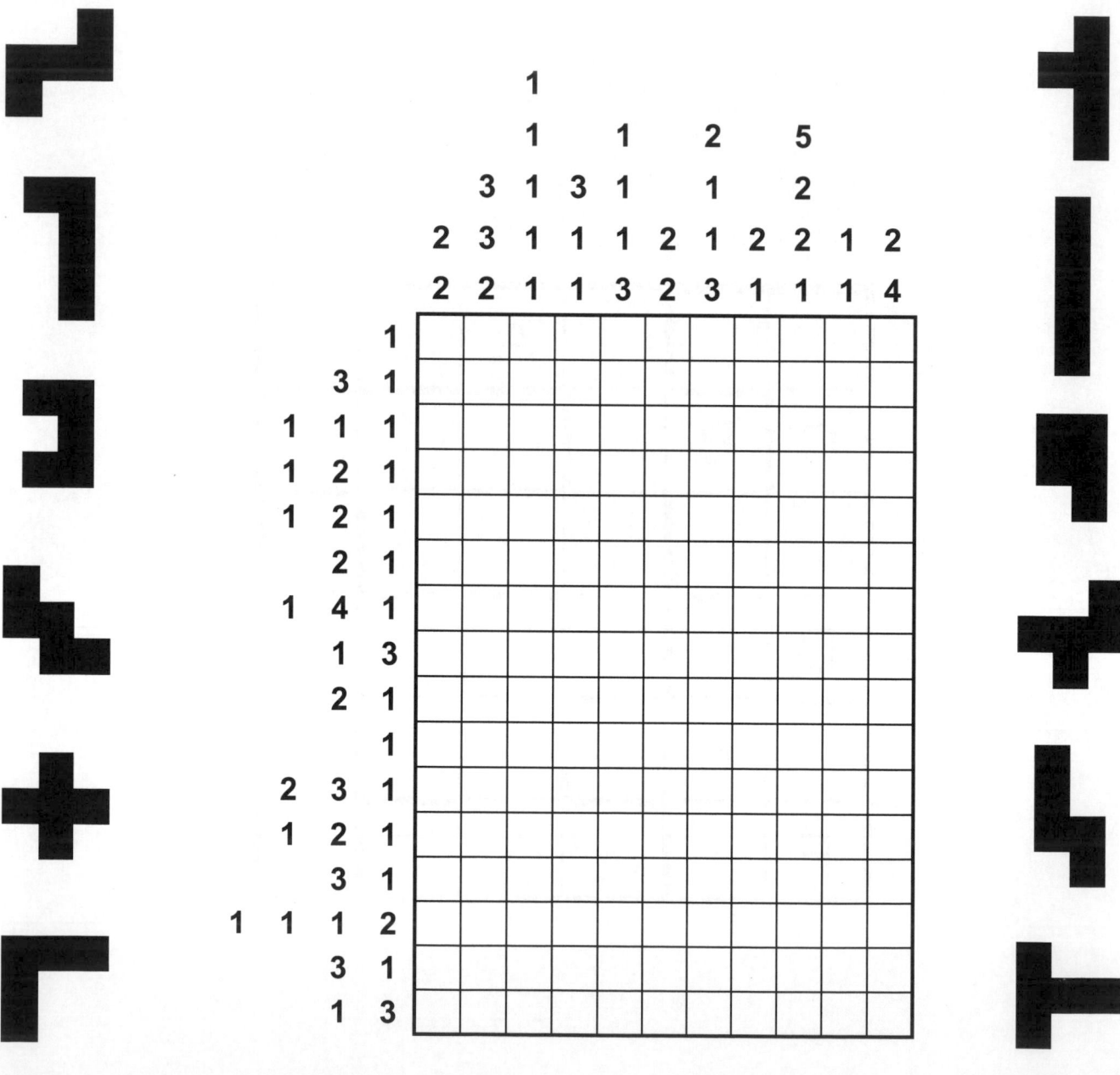

Tile Twister

Place the eight tiles into the puzzle grid so that all adjacent numbers on each tile match up. Tiles may be rotated through 360 degrees, but none may be flipped over.

2	1
2	4

4	1
2	3

3	2
3	2

1	4
4	2

		1	1		
		2	4		

3	3
2	1

2	2
1	3

1	2
4	4

1	4
3	1

Domino Placement

A standard set of twenty-eight dominoes has been laid out as shown. Can you draw in the edges of them all? The check-box is provided as an aid, so that you can see which dominoes have been located.

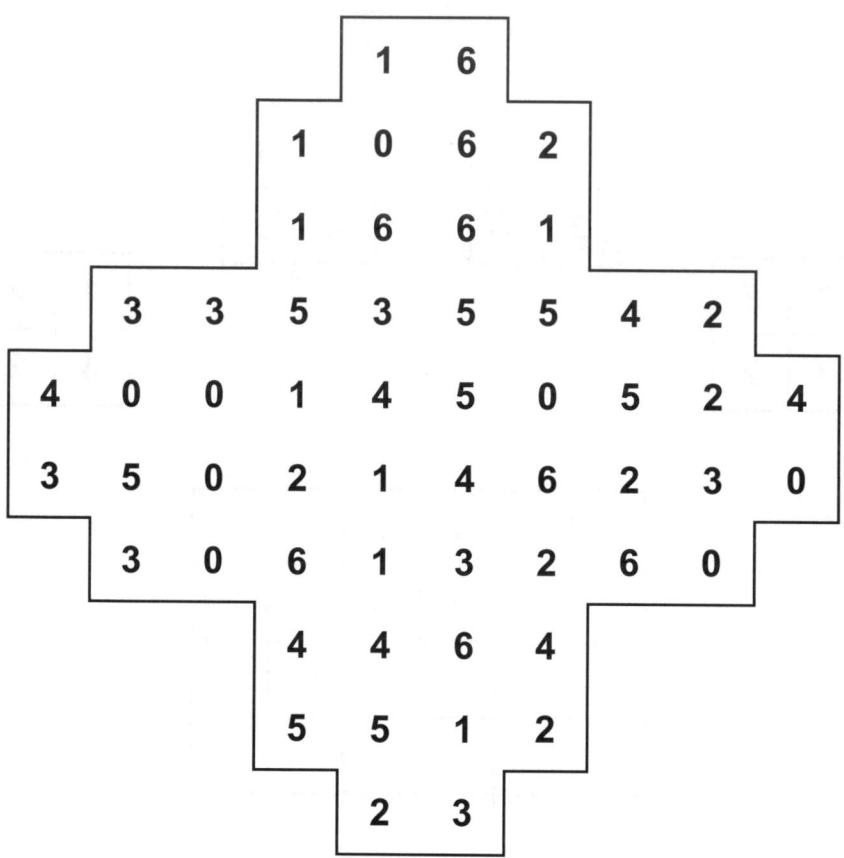

0-0	0-1	0-2	0-3	0-4	0-5	0-6	1-1	1-2	1-3	1-4	1-5	1-6	2-2

2-3	2-4	2-5	2-6	3-3	3-4	3-5	3-6	4-4	4-5	4-6	5-5	5-6	6-6

Hexagony

Can you place the hexagons into the grid, so that where any hexagon touches another along a straight line, the contents of both triangles is the same? No rotation of any hexagon is allowed!

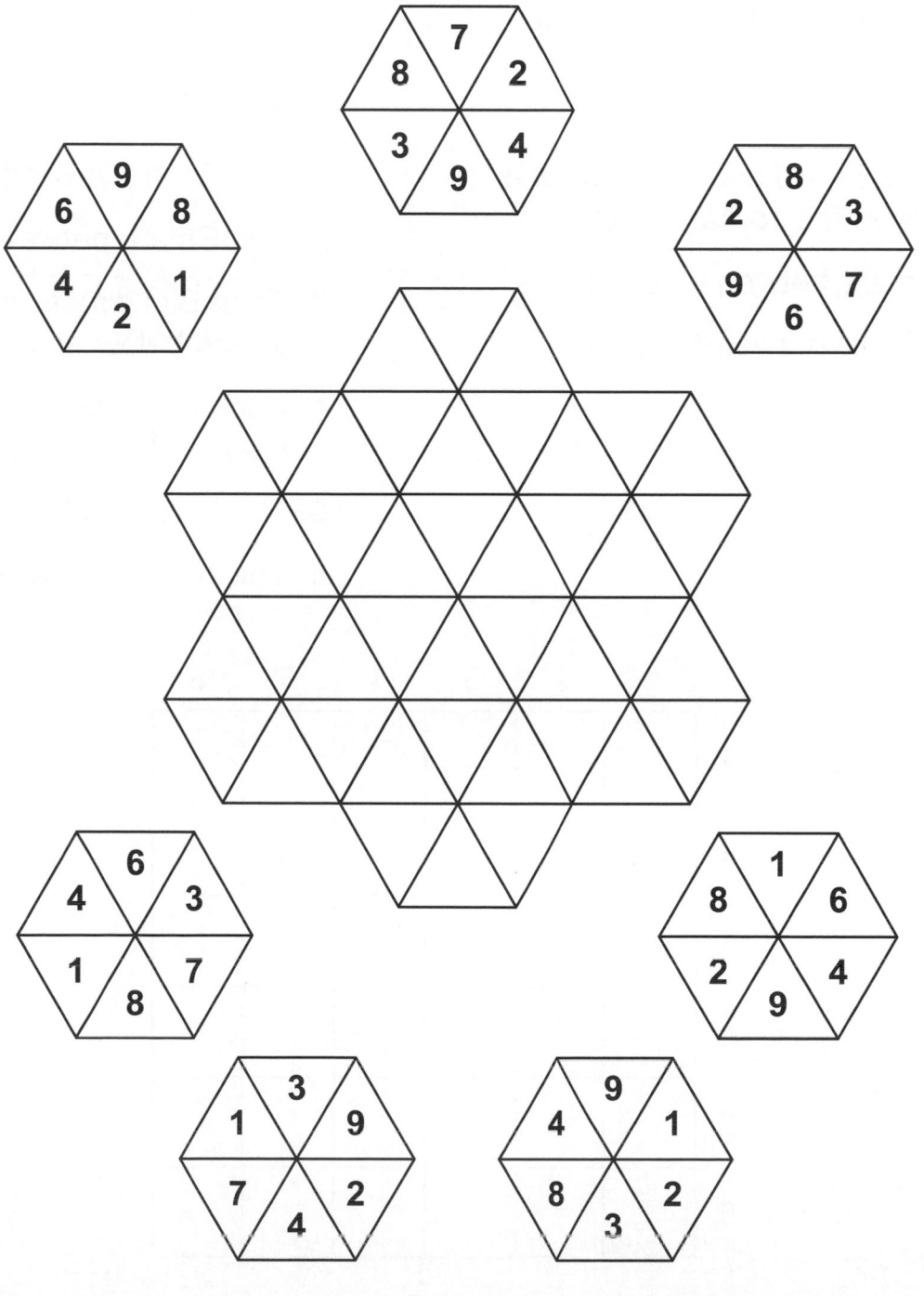

Simple as A, B, C?

Each of the small squares in the grid below contains either A, B or C. Every row, column and each of the two long diagonals has exactly two of each letter. The information in the clues refers only to the squares in that row or column. To help you solve this problem, we have provided as many clues as we think you will need! Can you tell the letter in each square?

Across

1 The two Bs are separated by one square, which contains a C.

5 The Bs are between the Cs.

6 The Cs are between the As.

Down

1 The Bs are lower than the As.

2 The Cs are between the As.

3 Each B is directly next to and below an A.

4 Each C is directly next to and below an A.

5 The Bs are between the Cs.

6 The As are between the Bs.

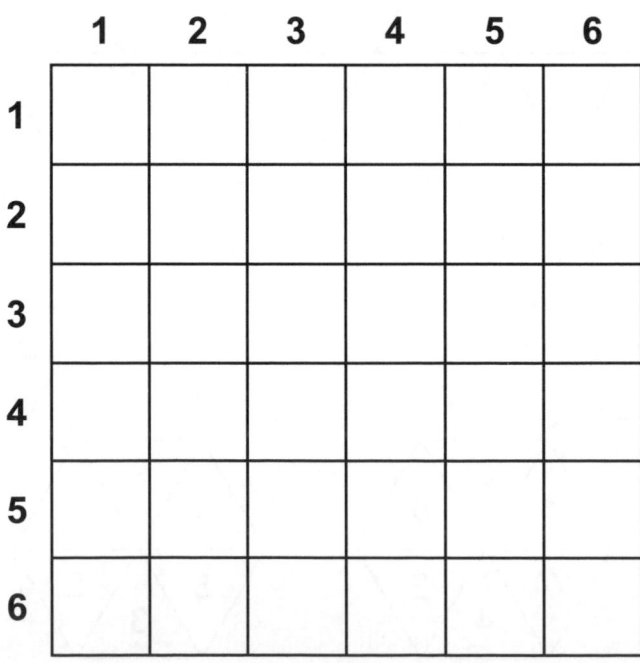

Total Concentration

The blank squares below should be filled with whole numbers between 1 and 40 inclusive, any of which may occur more than once, or not at all. The numbers in every horizontal row add up to the totals on the right, as do the two long diagonal lines; whilst those in every vertical column add up to the totals along the bottom. Can you discover the missing numbers?

								234
9	15	26	18	4		9	26	125
	34	23	12	19	9		35	196
27		25	24	39	39	17		212
14	36		12	34	29		13	189
15	2	3			38		6	125
30	7	34			18	7	34	167
		12	23	24		18		104
37	33	38	12	20		7	35	186
170	163	174	145	191	166	129	166	178

Shape Up

Every row and column in this grid originally contained one circle, one diamond, one square, one triangle and two blank squares, although not necessarily in that order.

Every symbol with a black arrow refers to the first of the four symbols encountered when travelling in the direction of the arrow. Every symbol with a white arrow refers to the second of the four symbols encountered in the direction of the arrow. Can you complete the original grid?

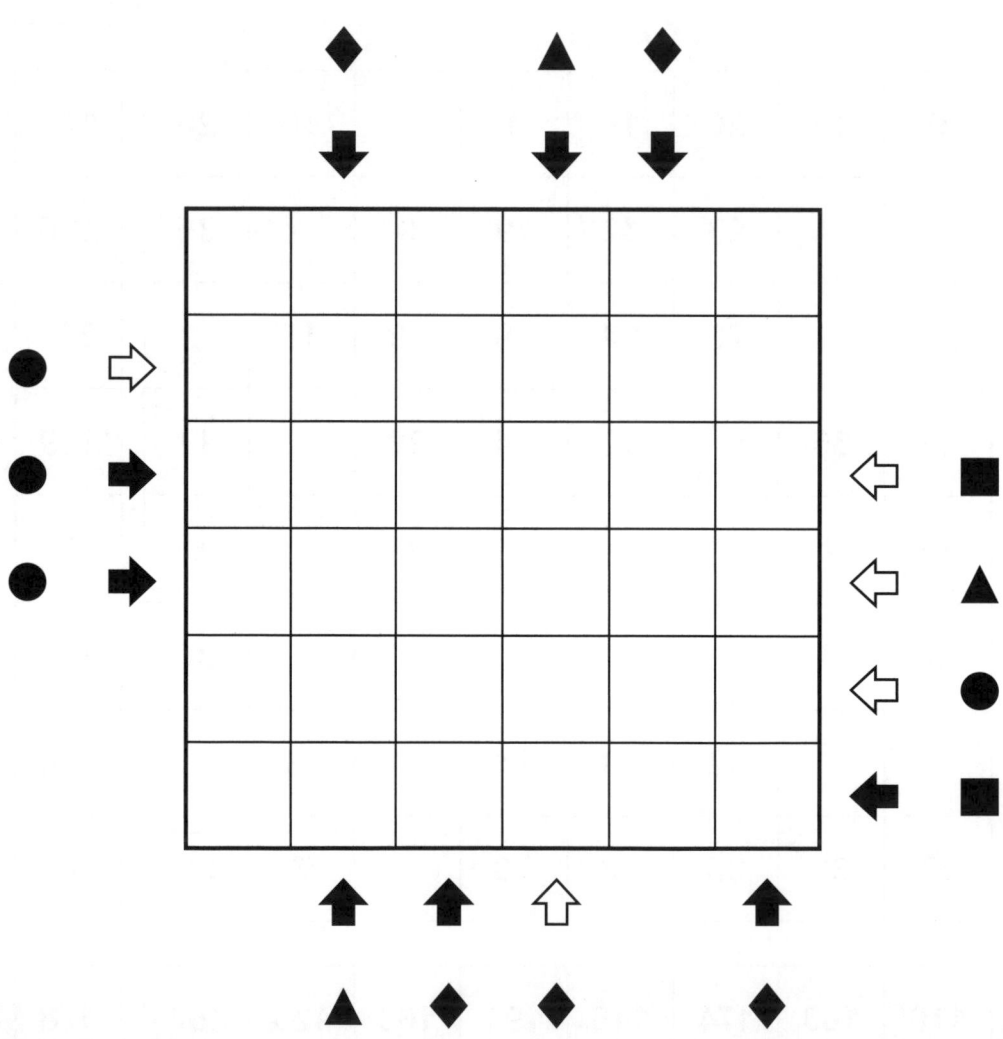

Given that the letters are valued 1-26 according to their places in the alphabet, can you crack the mystery code to reveal the missing letter?

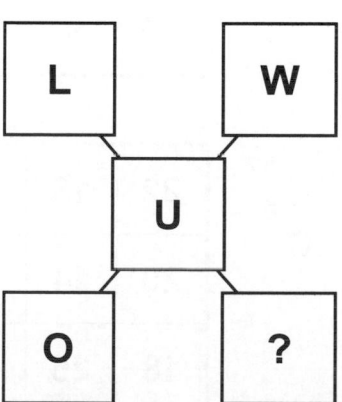

Whatever Next?

Which of the four lettered alternatives (A, B, C or D) fits most logically into the empty square?

1

16	15	18
10	11	13
21	19	17

2

21	17	22
13	13	11
19	20	18

3

26	19	14
7	16	20
13	24	21

4

?

~~~~~~

A

17	19	21
16	15	17
15	9	18

B

14	17	23
18	19	19
16	10	22

C

22	16	19
20	14	8
18	26	19

D

16	15	28
7	26	13
20	17	19

The Bottom Line

Can you fill each square in the bottom line with the correct digit? Every square in the solution contains only one digit from each of the lettered lines above, although two or more squares in the solution may contain the same digit.

At the end of every row is a score, which shows:

a   the number of digits placed in the correct finishing position on the bottom line, as indicated by a tick; and

b   the number of digits which appear on the bottom line, but in a different position, as indicated by a cross.

SCORE

A	1	2	3	4	✗
B	5	6	2	7	✗
C	4	8	7	8	✗ ✗
D	8	3	4	5	✗ ✗
E	3	4	8	6	✓ ✗
					✓✓✓✓

Solutions

1

2

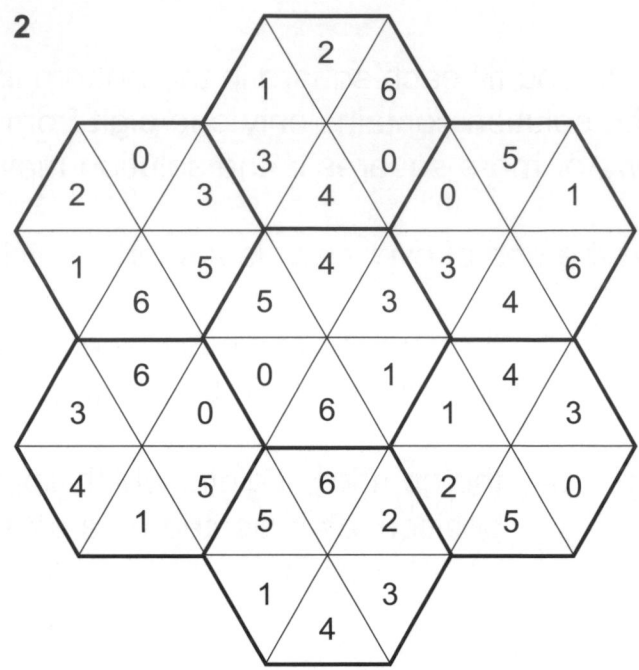

3

C	A	C	B	A	B
C	A	C	B	B	A
B	C	B	C	A	A
B	B	A	A	C	C
A	C	A	C	B	B
A	B	B	A	C	C

4

18	33	6	8	11	22	2	40
16	6	32	31	15	31	7	24
27	17	38	13	5	12	12	4
34	10	1	19	28	9	35	17
4	23	15	20	25	39	7	19
40	9	30	16	2	29	5	13
14	18	36	23	3	14	11	9
8	26	7	1	37	21	3	10

5

		♦	●	■	▲
■	▲			●	♦
	●	■	▲	♦	
●	♦			▲	■
♦		▲	■		●
▲	■	●	♦		

6

The sum total of the values of the letters in the outer squares minus the value of the letter in the central square is 50. Thus the missing value is 19, so the missing letter is S.

7

C – From stage to stage, the top row becomes the middle row, the middle row becomes the bottom row, and the bottom row becomes the top row, with letters move back one place in the alphabet each time (and with A changing to Z where it occurs.

Solutions

8

8374

9

10

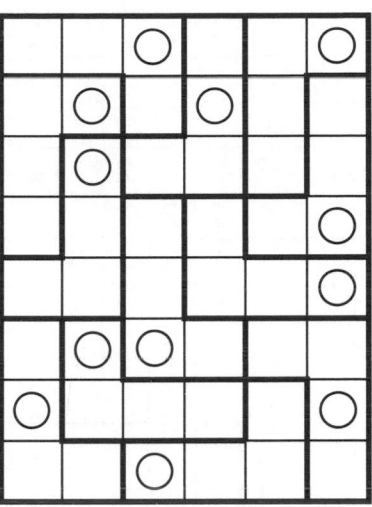

11

A

12

6	3	1	2	5	4
1	6	2	4	3	5
3	1	5	6	4	2
5	4	3	1	2	6
2	5	4	3	6	1
4	2	6	5	1	3

13

D6

14

15

Solutions

16

17

8 – Multiply the quantities in scale B by two, so that 4 hearts + 2 spades = 4 diamonds. Now replace these 2 spades with their value in scale A, so that 1 heart + 2 diamonds + 4 hearts = 4 diamonds; thus 5 hearts + 2 diamonds. In scale A, replace the 2 diamonds with 5 hearts, so that 5 hearts + 1 heart = 2 spades. So 3 hearts = 1 spade. Since 2 diamonds = 5 hearts and 1 spade = 3 hearts (above), a total of 8 hearts are needed to balance scale C.

18

F	C	E	D	B	A
A	B	C	E	F	D
C	D	F	A	E	B
B	F	D	C	A	E
D	E	A	B	C	F
E	A	B	F	D	C

19

20

4	1	1	3	3	1
2	4	4	4	4	2
2	4	4	4	4	2
3	1	1	2	2	3
3	1	1	2	2	3
1	2	2	2	2	4

Solutions

21

22

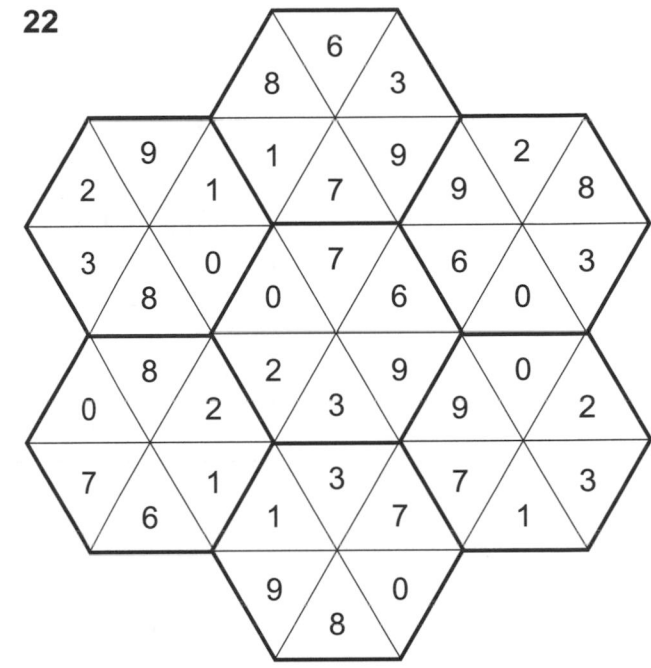

23

A	C	B	A	C	B
A	C	B	C	B	A
B	A	C	C	A	B
C	B	A	B	A	C
B	A	C	A	B	C
C	B	A	B	C	A

24

14	25	11	9	37	32	34	2
10	11	13	5	34	25	2	26
35	26	39	6	5	1	22	25
1	18	21	34	40	7	27	15
26	21	23	27	19	34	19	11
37	16	30	34	11	34	2	24
15	1	37	38	30	20	6	4
6	12	8	33	22	21	10	4

25

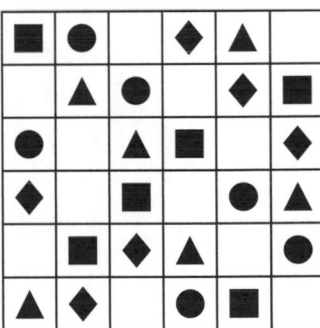

26

The value of the central letter is the total value of the two letters in the highest boxes, minus the total value of the two letters in the lowest boxes. Thus the missing value is 2, so the missing letter is B.

27

A – All numerical values are divisible by 5.

Solutions

28
3185

29

30
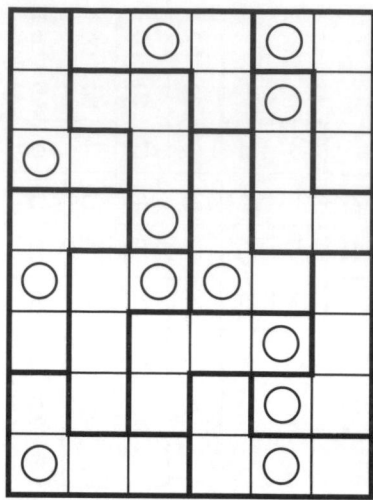

31
D

32

6	5	3	1	4	2
3	2	1	5	6	4
2	1	4	6	5	3
4	6	5	2	3	1
1	3	6	4	2	5
5	4	2	3	1	6

33
E5

34
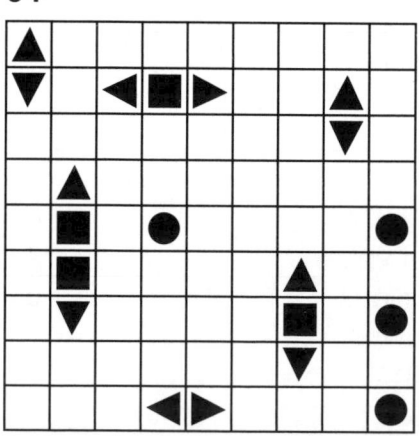

35

					●	2		2	
	0	1	●		3	4	●	3	●
	0		1		●	●		4	●
			1		●			●	2
2	●	●				3	2		
	●	4				2	3	●	
2	●		0		●	●	●		●
2			2	1		3	4	4	●
●		●		●		●	3	●	
	2	1	2		●	3	●	2	

Solutions

36

```
          3  1  .  1  2
       1  1        .  0 . 2
   2        1     1        2
   2  1  0        3  1
   2     1  1  3  1     1
       1  2        1
          1  3  1  2     1
       2  2
   3  3  2     1     1    1  2
       1              1  1
   3     3  1     .  1  0     2
          1     3  3
```

37

16 – Substitute the 2 spades in scale B with their value (ie 2 hearts + 4 diamonds) in scale A, so that 3 diamonds + 2 hearts + 4 diamonds = 3 hearts (scale B). Thus 7 diamonds = 1 heart. In scale A, 2 diamonds + 1 heart = 1 spade – and 1 heart = 7 diamonds (above), so 9 diamonds = 1 spade. There is 1 heart (the same as 7 diamonds, above) and 1 spade (the same as 9 diamonds, above) in scale C. Thus 16 diamonds are needed to balance scale C.

38

D	A	E	F	C	B
C	B	A	D	F	E
F	E	B	A	D	C
A	C	F	B	E	D
B	D	C	E	A	F
E	F	D	C	B	A

39

40

1	2	2	2	2	3
1	4	4	2	2	3
1	4	4	2	2	3
3	3	3	2	2	1
3	3	3	2	2	1
1	4	4	4	4	3

Solutions

41

42

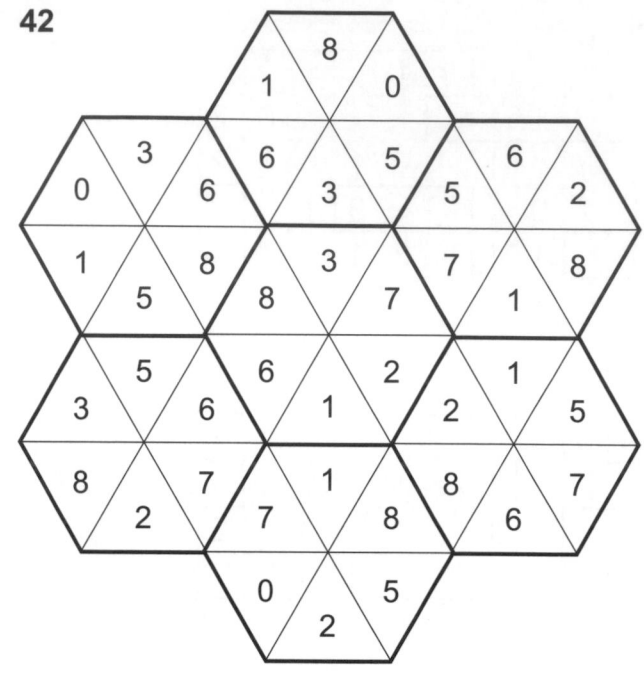

43

A	A	C	B	B	C
C	B	A	C	B	A
B	B	C	C	A	A
B	C	B	A	A	C
C	A	B	A	C	B
A	C	A	B	C	B

44

5	32	26	36	9	6	24	14
13	30	25	31	29	17	24	13
7	9	31	2	31	31	11	25
29	9	16	2	17	28	22	22
24	23	2	9	33	30	24	2
11	19	15	1	25	39	35	30
21	3	33	38	17	16	37	8
14	25	29	22	32	13	27	26

45

●		■	▲		◆
▲	◆			●	■
◆		●	■		▲
	●	▲	◆	■	
■	▲			◆	●
	■	◆	●	▲	

46

The value of the central letter is the total of the other four letters. Thus the missing value is 4, so the missing letter is D.

47

D – Each letter in the top row moves back one place in the alphabet, whilst the others move forward two places in the alphabet every time.

Solutions

48

5148

49

50

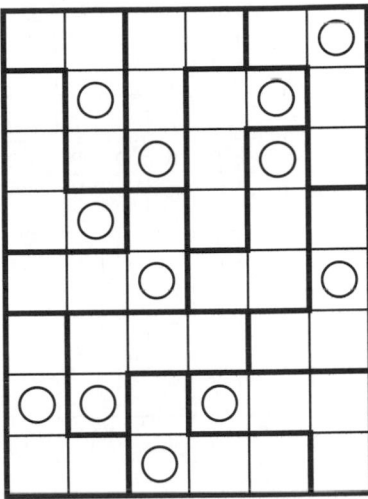

51

B

52

6	2	1	4	3	5
1	4	5	2	6	3
4	6	3	1	5	2
3	5	4	6	2	1
2	3	6	5	1	4
5	1	2	3	4	6

53

C5

54

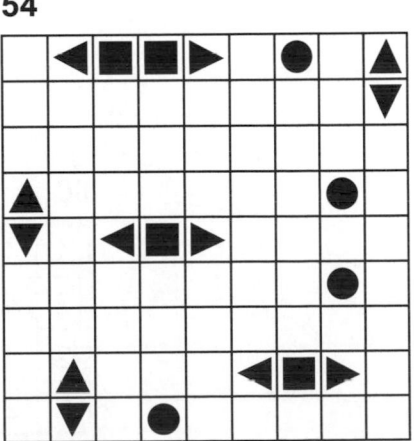

55

		0			0		●		
0							1		0
			2		1	0			
	3			●	●			●	
●	●	●	●	●	3		2	2	
	5			3	●	1		●	
●	2	●	1				●		4
	5				●	●	●	●	●
●	●	●	1	3	●		4	4	
	3			●	2		●		

Solutions

56

57

16 – Multiply the quantities in scale B by five, so that 5 clubs + 10 hearts = 20 spades. Now replace the 5 clubs in scale B with their value in scale A, so that 12 hearts = 14 spades, thus 6 hearts = 7 spades, and 36 hearts = 42 spades. Multiply scale A by seven, so that 14 hearts + 42 spades = 35 clubs. Now replace these 42 spades with 36 hearts, so that 14 hearts + 36 hearts = 35 clubs, thus 50 hearts = 35 clubs. So 10 hearts = 7 clubs. there are 7 spades (the same as 6 hearts, above) and 7 clubs (the same as 10 hearts, above) in scale C. Thus a total of 16 hearts are needed to balance scale C.

58

E	F	B	A	D	C
F	A	D	C	B	E
B	C	A	F	E	D
C	D	E	B	F	A
A	E	F	D	C	B
D	B	C	E	A	F

59

60

1	4	4	2	2	1
2	4	4	3	3	1
2	4	4	3	3	1
2	2	2	3	3	2
2	2	2	3	3	2
1	2	2	1	1	4

Solutions

61

62

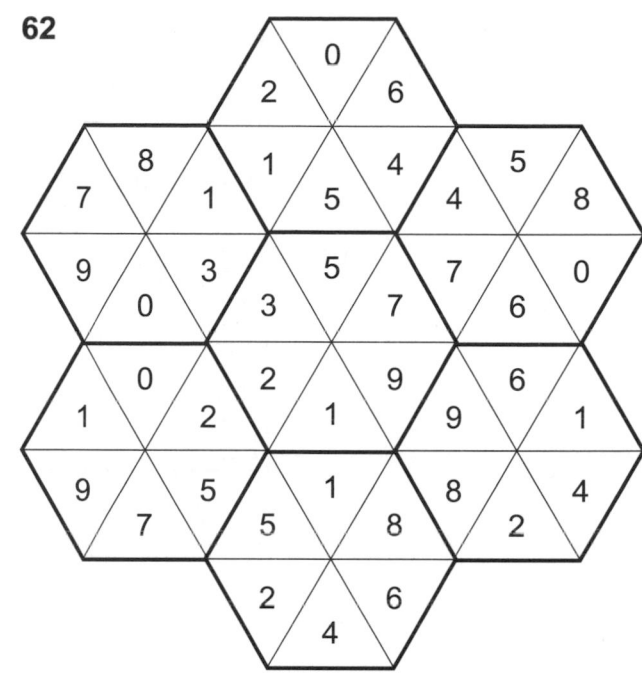

63

C	B	B	A	A	C
B	A	C	C	B	A
A	C	B	B	A	C
B	A	A	C	C	B
C	C	A	A	B	B
A	B	C	B	C	A

64

33	11	37	15	23	21	22	2
21	18	9	31	23	13	13	39
32	35	25	36	24	11	21	19
6	33	29	31	27	16	26	18
38	24	39	32	18	22	17	23
23	3	8	15	33	11	10	28
22	9	20	29	22	19	12	28
13	12	35	24	38	39	29	31

65

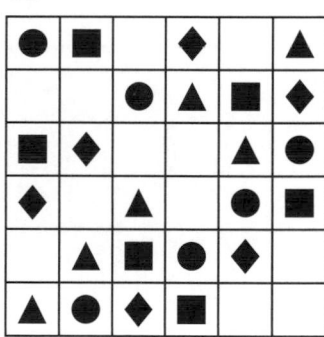

66

The value of the central letter is the value of the letter in the top left corner plus that in the bottom right corner, also that of the value of the letter in the top right corner plus that in the bottom left corner. Thus the missing value is 13, so the missing letter is M.

67

C – Reading from left to right, top to bottom, the numbers follow the sequence 5-3-6-1-7-4-2, then repeat, with the remaining numbers of the sequence appearing in a different square.

Solutions

68

4378

69

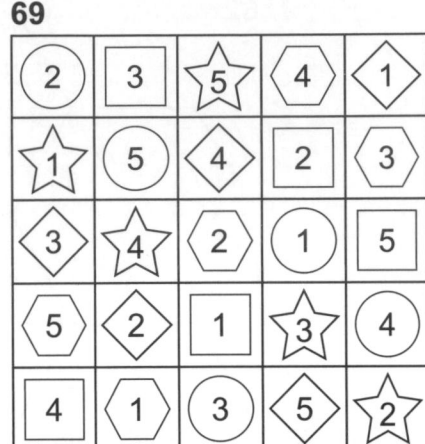

70

71

A

72

6	5	2	4	3	1
4	6	1	3	5	2
3	1	5	6	2	4
1	2	4	5	6	3
2	3	6	1	4	5
5	4	3	2	1	6

73

B6

74

75

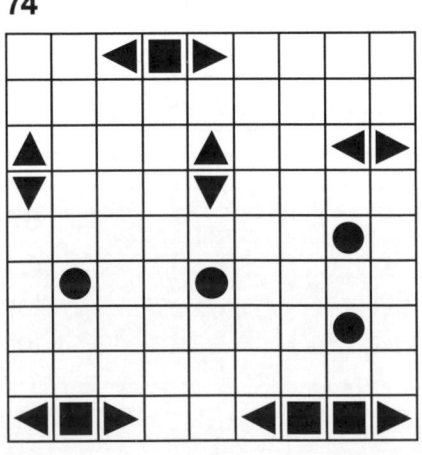

Solutions

76

```
  2 3   0     0
      3   1 2 3
  2 1   0     2 2
  3 1         1
    1   0   0
  2     1   2     0
3 2 1     1     1 1
  1   0 1   3
0 1 3   0 1   1
2   2 1 1 1 0   1 2
  1     2   1
  2     2     1 2 3
```

77

8 – Multiply the quantities in scale A by four, so that 4 hearts + 4 spades = 8 clubs, then replace these 4 hearts with their value in scale B, ie 1 club and 1 spade; so 1 club + 1 spade + 4 spades = 8 clubs. Thus 5 spades = 7 clubs. Now multiply the quantities in scale B by seven, so that 7 clubs + 7 spades = 28 hearts, then replace these 7 clubs with 5 spades (above). Thus (7 spades + 5 spades) 12 spades = 28 hearts. So 3 spades = 7 hearts. Scale C has 7 clubs (the same as 5 spades, above) + 7 hearts (the same as 3 spades, above), so 8 spades are needed to balance scale C.

78

F	E	B	A	D	C
D	C	F	B	A	E
A	F	D	E	C	B
E	B	A	C	F	D
C	A	E	D	B	F
B	D	C	F	E	A

79

80

1	3	3	3	3	2
2	4	4	1	1	1
2	4	4	1	1	1
1	3	3	2	2	4
1	3	3	2	2	4
3	2	2	3	3	3

Solutions

81

82

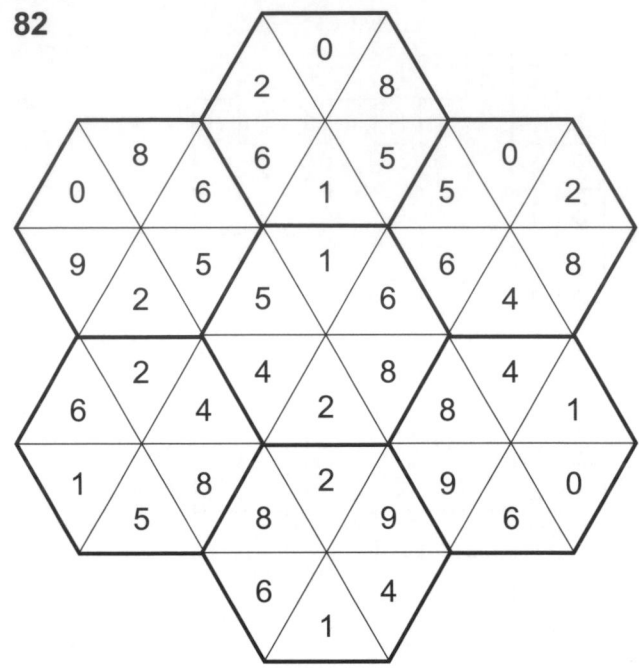

83

C	B	A	A	B	C
A	B	C	C	A	B
B	C	A	B	A	C
A	C	B	B	C	A
B	A	C	A	C	B
C	A	B	C	B	A

84

22	9	40	37	37	9	34	7
39	2	31	18	36	37	36	8
38	39	8	8	2	30	30	19
35	22	10	27	7	7	34	16
24	29	1	38	38	6	27	10
6	31	2	9	12	21	40	39
30	14	16	27	25	39	2	18
38	7	35	8	12	24	20	31

85

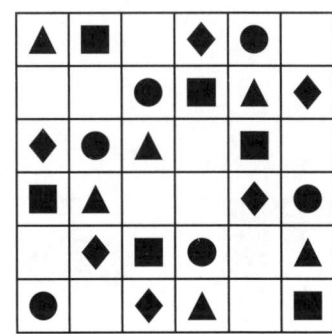

86

The value of the central letter is the total value of the two letters in the furthest left boxes multiplied by the total value of the two letters in the furthest right boxes. Thus the missing value is 4, so the missing letter is D.

87

A – The letters are given numerical values according to their positions in the alphabet. These values, together with the number in the central square, are all prime numbers.

Solutions

88

3553

89

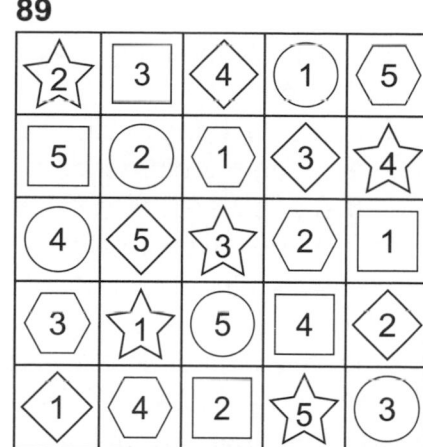

90

91

E

92

5	3	1	2	4	6
4	5	3	1	6	2
2	6	5	3	1	4
1	4	6	5	2	3
3	2	4	6	5	1
6	1	2	4	3	5

93

F7

94

95

Solutions

96

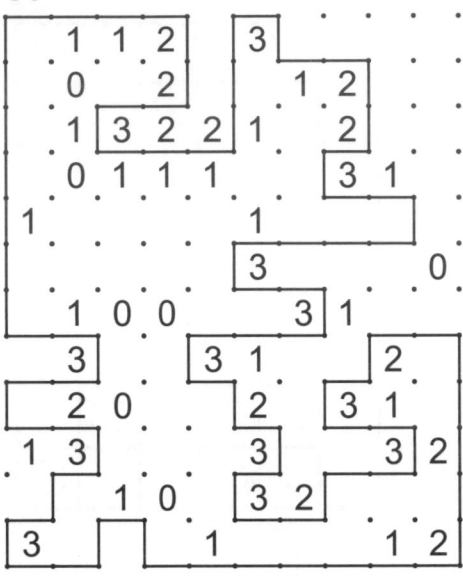

97

3 – Multiply the quantities in scale B by three, so that 3 diamonds + 6 hearts = 9 spades. Now replace these 6 hearts with their value in scale A, so that 1 diamond + 1 spade + 3 diamonds = 9 spades. Thus 4 diamonds = 8 spades, so 2 diamonds = 4 spades and 1 diamond = 2 spades. Now multiply the quantities in scale A by two, so that 2 diamonds + 2 spades = 12 hearts. Now replace these 2 spades with 1 diamond (above), so that 2 diamonds + 1 diamond = 12 hearts, so 1 diamond = 4 hearts. There are 4 spades (the same as 2 diamonds, above) and 4 hearts (the same as 1 diamond (above) in scale C. So a total of 3 diamonds are needed to balance scale C.

98

B	F	D	A	E	C
C	B	F	E	D	A
E	A	C	B	F	D
D	C	E	F	A	B
A	E	B	D	C	F
F	D	A	C	B	E

99

100

3	1	1	1	1	4
2	2	2	4	4	2
2	2	2	4	4	2
3	3	3	1	1	2
3	3	3	1	1	2
2	1	1	4	4	4

Solutions

101

102

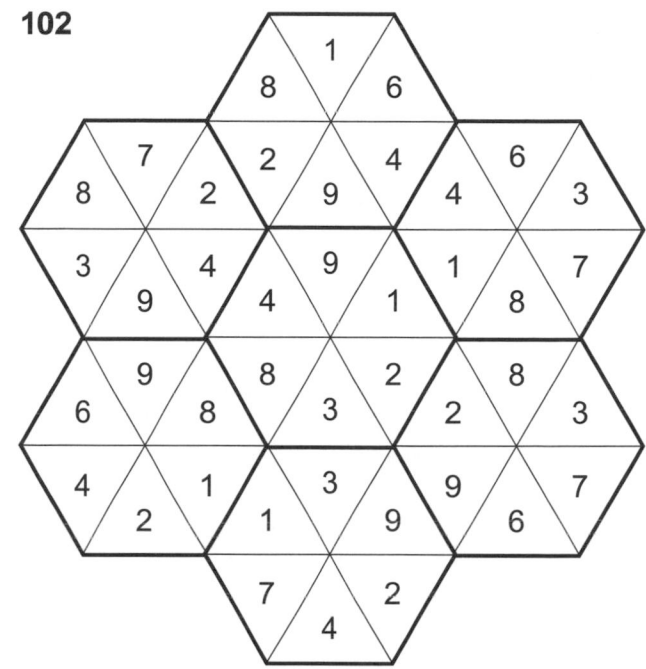

103

A	B	C	B	A	C
C	A	A	B	C	B
A	C	B	A	B	C
B	C	A	C	B	A
C	B	B	A	C	A
B	A	C	C	A	B

104

9	15	26	18	4	18	9	26
34	34	23	12	19	9	30	35
27	33	25	24	39	39	17	8
14	36	13	12	34	29	38	13
15	2	3	31	27	38	3	6
30	7	34	13	24	18	7	34
4	3	12	23	24	11	18	9
37	33	38	12	20	4	7	35

105

■	♦		▲		●
♦	●	■			▲
●		▲	■	♦	
		●	♦	▲	■
▲	■			●	♦
	▲	♦	●	■	

106

The value of the central letter is the total value of the letters in the top left, bottom left and bottom right squares, minus the value of the letter in the top right square. Thus the missing value is 17, so the missing letter is Q.

107

C – The totals of the left and right columns when subtracted from the totals of the top and bottom rows gives the number in the central square.

Solutions

108
7783